TEACHER EDITION • Chapter 8
Two-Digit Addition and Subtraction

Houghton Mifflin Harcourt

Curious George by Margret and H.A. Rey. Copyright © 2010 by Houghton Mifflin Harcourt Publishing Company. All rights reserved. The character Curious George®, including without limitation the character's name and the character's likenesses, are registered trademarks of Houghton Mifflin Harcourt Publishing Company.

Copyright © 2015 by Houghton Mifflin Harcourt Publishing Company

Printed in the U.S.A.

ISBN 978-0-544-29571-1

11 12 13 14 15 16 0029 23 22 21 20 19 18
4500696241   DEFG

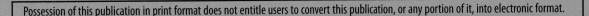

Critical Area | Number and Operations in Base Ten

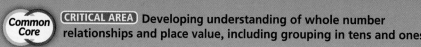 CRITICAL AREA Developing understanding of whole number relationships and place value, including grouping in tens and ones

Chapter 6   **Count and Model Numbers** 327

Chapter 7   **Compare Numbers** 395

Chapter 8   **Two-Digit Addition and Subtraction** 433

Lessons   **Grade 1 Common Core State Standards**

Domain: Operations and Algebraic Thinking   1.OA

Cluster C: **Add and subtract within 20.**

8.1 ◼

1.OA.C.6   Add and subtract within 20, demonstrating fluency for addition and subtraction within 10. Use strategies such as counting on; making ten (e.g., 8 + 6 = 8 + 2 + 4 = 10 + 4 = 14); decomposing a number leading to a ten (e.g., 13 − 4 5 13 − 3 − 1 5 10 − 1 5 9); using the relationship between addition and subtraction (e.g., knowing that 8 + 4 = 12, one knows 12 − 8 = 4); and creating equivalent but easier or known sums (e.g., adding 6 + 7 by creating the known equivalent 6 + 6 + 1 = 12 + 1 = 13).

Domain: Number and Operations in Base Ten   1.NBT

Cluster C: **Use place value understanding and properties of operations to add and subtract.**

8.2, 8.4–8.10 ◼

1.NBT.C.4   Add within 100, including adding a two-digit number and a one-digit number, and adding a two-digit number and a multiple of 10, using concrete models or drawings and strategies based on place value, properties of operations, and/or the relationship between addition and subtraction; relate the strategy to a written method and explain the reasoning used. Understand that in adding two-digit numbers, one adds tens and tens, ones and ones; and sometimes it is necessary to compose a ten.

8.3, 8.10 ◼

1.NBT.C.6   Subtract multiples of 10 in the range 10–90 from multiples of 10 in the range 10–90 (positive or zero differences), using concrete models or drawings and strategies based on place value, properties of operations, and/or the relationship between addition and subtraction; relate the strategy to a written method and explain the reasoning used.

Key: Major Clusters: ◼   Supporting Clusters: ☐   Additional Clusters: ○

Table of Contents

Chapter 8 Two-Digit Addition and Subtraction

Domains:

Operations and Algebraic Thinking	**1.OA**
Number and Operations in Base Ten	**1.NBT**

Common Core MATHEMATICAL PRACTICES

MP1 Make sense of problems and persevere in solving them.

MP2 Reason abstractly and quantitatively.

MP3 Construct viable arguments and critique the reasoning of others.

MP4 Model with mathematics.

MP5 Use appropriate tools strategically.

MP6 Attend to precision.

MP7 Look for and make use of structure.

MP8 Look for and express regularity in repeated reasoning.

Planning   Page

	Page
Chapter At A Glance	433A
Teaching for Depth	433E
Daily Classroom Management	433F
Strategies for English Language Learners	433G
Developing Math Language	433H
Review Prerequisite Skills	433I
Common Core Focus and Coherence: Learning Progressions and Content Standards	433J
Introduce the Chapter	433
Show What You Know	434
Vocabulary Builder	435
Game	436

Lessons   Common Core State Standards   Page

		Common Core State Standards	Page
8.1	Add and Subtract within 20	1.OA.C.6	437A
8.2	Hands On • Add Tens	1.NBT.C.4	443A
8.3	Hands On • Subtract Tens	1.NBT.C.6	449A
	Mid-Chapter Checkpoint		452
8.4	Use a Hundred Chart to Add	1.NBT.C.4	455A
8.5	Hands On • Use Models to Add	1.NBT.C.4	461A
8.6	Hands On • Make Ten to Add	1.NBT.C.4	467A
8.7	Hands On • Use Place Value to Add	1.NBT.C.4	473A
8.8	Problem Solving • Addition Word Problems	1.NBT.C.4	479A
8.9	Related Addition and Subtraction	1.NBT.C.4	485A
8.10	Practice Addition and Subtraction	1.NBT.C.4, 1.NBT.C.6	491A
	Chapter 8 Review/Test		497–498
	Chapter 8 Test		500A

Chapter At A Glance

Domains: Operations and Algebraic Thinking
Number and Operations in Base Ten

Chapter Essential Question How can you add and subtract two-digit numbers?

Use the *GO Math! Planning Guide* for correlations, mathematical practices information, and more.

	I Day LESSON 8.1 I.OA.C.6	I Day LESSON 8.2 I.NBT.C.4	I Day LESSON 8.3 I.NBT.C.6
Lesson At A Glance	Add and Subtract within 20 . . . . . . 437A	Hands On • Add Tens 443A	Hands On • Subtract Tens 449A
Essential Question	What strategies can you use to add and subtract?	How can you add tens?	How can you subtract tens?
Objective	Add and subtract within 20.	Draw a model to add tens.	Draw a model to subtract tens.
Vocabulary			
ELL Strategy	**ELL** Strategy • Scaffold Language	**ELL** Strategy • Understand Context	**ELL** Strategy • Understand Context

GO DIGITAL Go online to access all your chapter resources

www.thinkcentral.com

8.1 *i*Student Edition	8.2 *i*Student Edition	8.3 *i*Student Edition
8.1 *e*Teacher Edition	8.2 *e*Teacher Edition	8.3 *e*Teacher Edition
Personal Math Trainer	Personal Math Trainer	Personal Math Trainer
Math on the Spot Video	Math on the Spot Video	Math on the Spot Video
*i*Tools	Animated Math Models	Animated Math Models
HMH Mega Math	*i*Tools	*i*Tools
	HMH Mega Math	HMH Mega Math

Print Resources

8.1 Student Edition	8.2 Student Edition	8.3 Student Edition
8.1 Practice and Homework (in the *Student Edition*)	8.2 Practice and Homework (in the *Student Edition*)	8.3 Practice and Homework (in the *Student Edition*)
8.1 Reteach (in the *Chapter Resources*)	8.2 Reteach (in the *Chapter Resources*)	8.3 Reteach (in the *Chapter Resources*)
8.1 Enrich (in the *Chapter Resources*)	8.2 Enrich (in the *Chapter Resources*)	8.3 Enrich (in the *Chapter Resources*)
Grab-and-Go™ Centers Kit	Grab-and-Go™ Centers Kit	Grab-and-Go™ Centers Kit

RtI

Response to Intervention

Before the Chapter	During the Lesson	After the Chapter
✓ **Show What You Know**	✓ **Share and Show**	✓ **Chapter Review/Test**
• Prerequisite Skills Activities • Personal Math Trainer	• Reteach • Mid-Chapter Checkpoint • Personal Math Trainer • Reteach Activity (online)	• Reteach • Personal Math Trainer • Reteach Activity (online)

1 Day
LESSON 8.4 ■ 1.NBT.C.4

Use a Hundred Chart to Add 455A

How can you use a hundred chart to count on by ones or tens?

Use a hundred chart to find sums.

ELL Strategy • Model Concepts

---

1 Day
LESSON 8.5 ■ 1.NBT.C.4

Hands On • Use Models to Add...........461A

How can models help you add ones or tens to a two-digit number?

Use concrete models to add ones or tens to a two-digit number.

ELL Strategy • Understand Context

---

2 Days
LESSON 8.6 ■ 1.NBT.C.4

Hands On • Make Ten to Add 467A

How can making a ten help you add a two-digit number and a one-digit number?

Make a ten to add a two-digit number and a one-digit number.

ELL Strategy • Understand Context

8.4 *i*Student Edition

8.4 *e*Teacher Edition

Personal Math Trainer

Math on the Spot Video

*i*T *i*Tools

8.5 *i*Student Edition

8.5 *e*Teacher Edition

Personal Math Trainer

Math on the Spot Video

Animated Math Models

*i*T *i*Tools

8.6 *i*Student Edition

8.6 *e*Teacher Edition

Personal Math Trainer

Math on the Spot Video

Animated Math Models

*i*T *i*Tools

HMH Mega Math

8.4 Student Edition

8.4 Practice and Homework
   (in the *Student Edition*)

8.4 Reteach (in the *Chapter Resources*)

8.4 Enrich (in the *Chapter Resources*)

Grab-and-Go™ Centers Kit

8.5 Student Edition

8.5 Practice and Homework
   (in the *Student Edition*)

8.5 Reteach (in the *Chapter Resources*)

8.5 Enrich (in the *Chapter Resources*)

Grab-and-Go™ Centers Kit

8.6 Student Edition

8.6 Practice and Homework
   (in the *Student Edition*)

8.6 Reteach (in the *Chapter Resources*)

8.6 Enrich (in the *Chapter Resources*)

Grab-and-Go™ Centers Kit

 GO DIGITAL **Resources** *www.thinkcentral.com*

 Interactive Student Edition

 Personal Math Trainer

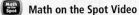 Math on the Spot Video

Animated Math Models

 Assessment

 HMH Mega Math

*i*T *i*Tools

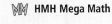 Multimedia *e*Glossary

Professional Development Videos

Chapter At A Glance

Domains: Operations and Algebraic Thinking
Number and Operations in Base Ten

Lesson At A Glance

	2 Days LESSON 8.7 — 1.NBT.C.4 Hands On • Use Place Value to Add ... 473A	**2 Days** LESSON 8.8 — 1.NBT.C.4 Problem Solving • Addition Word Problems 479A	**2 Days** LESSON 8.9 — 1.NBT.C.4 Related Addition and Subtraction 485A
Essential Question	How can you model tens and ones to help you add two-digit numbers?	How can drawing a picture help you explain how to solve an addition problem?	How can you use a hundred chart to show the relationship between addition and subtraction?
Objective	Use tens and ones to add two-digit numbers.	Solve and explain two-digit addition word problems using the strategy *draw a picture*.	Use a hundred chart to find sums and differences.
Vocabulary			
ELL Strategy	**ELL** Strategy • Illustrate Understanding	**ELL** Strategy • Rephrase	**ELL** Strategy • Illustrate Understanding

GO DIGITAL — Go online to access all your chapter resources

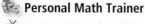

www.thinkcentral.com

8.7 iStudent Edition	8.8 iStudent Edition	8.9 iStudent Edition
8.7 eTeacher Edition	8.8 eTeacher Edition	8.9 eTeacher Edition
🐾 Personal Math Trainer	🐾 Personal Math Trainer	🐾 Personal Math Trainer
📺 Math on the Spot Video	📺 Math on the Spot Video	📺 Math on the Spot Video
📋 Animated Math Models	iT iTools	iT iTools
iT iTools	👑 HMH Mega Math	

Print Resources

8.7 Student Edition	8.8 Student Edition	8.9 Student Edition
8.7 Practice and Homework (in the *Student Edition*)	8.8 Practice and Homework (in the *Student Edition*)	8.9 Practice and Homework (in the *Student Edition*)
8.7 Reteach (in the *Chapter Resources*)	8.8 Reteach (in the *Chapter Resources*)	8.9 Reteach (in the *Chapter Resources*)
8.7 Enrich (in the *Chapter Resources*)	8.8 Enrich (in the *Chapter Resources*)	8.9 Enrich (in the *Chapter Resources*)
Grab-and-Go™ Centers Kit	Grab-and-Go™ Centers Kit	Grab-and-Go™ Centers Kit

Assessment

Diagnostic	**Formative**	**Summative**
• **Show What You Know**	• **Lesson Quick Check**	• **Chapter Review/Test**
• **Diagnostic Interview Task**	• **Mid-Chapter Checkpoint**	• **Chapter Test**
• **Digital Personal Math Trainer**	• **Digital Personal Math Trainer**	• **Performance Assessment Task**
	- *Assessment Animation*	• **Digital Personal Math Trainer**
	- *Assessment Video*	

I Day

LESSON 8.10

■ I.NBT.C.4

■ I.NBT.C.6

Practice Addition and Subtraction 491A

What different ways can you use to add and subtract?

Add and subtract within 100, including continued practice with facts within 20.

ELL **Strategy** • Cooperative Grouping

8.10 *i*Student Edition

8.10 *e*Teacher Edition

✓ Chapter 8 Test

Personal Math Trainer

Math on the Spot Video

Animated Math Models

iT *i*Tools

8.10 Student Edition

8.10 Practice and Homework
   (in the *Student Edition*)

8.10 Reteach (in the *Chapter Resources*)

8.10 Enrich (in the *Chapter Resources*)

Grab-and-Go™ Centers Kit

Teacher Notes

PROFESSIONAL DEVELOPMENT

Teaching for Depth

Steven J. Leinwand
Principal Research Analyst
American Institutes for Research (AIR)
Washington, D.C.

Learning to Add

The number system is embedded within the concept of adding. For instance, the pattern in counting numbers is to increase by one from one number to the next.

- Children explore the concept of adding, building awareness of what it means to add and the effect that adding has on a number.

- As competency with addition increases, children can transfer their understanding to other contexts such as exploring numbers in a hundred chart.

1	2	3	4	5	6	7	8	9	10
11	12	13	14	15	16	17	18	19	20
21	22	23	24	25	26	27	28	29	30
31	32	33	34	35	36	37	38	39	40
41	42	43	44	45	46	47	48	49	50
51	52	53	54	55	56	57	58	59	60
61	62	63	64	65	66	67	68	69	70
71	72	73	74	75	76	77	78	79	80
81	82	83	84	85	86	87	88	89	90
91	92	93	94	95	96	97	98	99	100

From the Research

❝…if we want children to "get" addition and subtraction, then we should encourage their work with those operations in ways that mimic how they are used in real life…❞

(Bahr & de Garcia, 2010, p. 84)

Learning to Subtract

Once children understand that two numbers added together (then called addends) result in a sum, they are ready to develop the next relationship between the addends and the sum.

- When working with related facts, children learn that subtracting one of the addends from the sum results in a difference that is the other addend.

- When children are presented with problem situations, they build their understanding of subtraction concepts.

- It is important to solve problems that represent a variety of contexts such as take away and compare.

Common Core

Mathematical Practices

As children learn addition and subtraction, they have an opportunity to use a variety of formal and informal models (e.g., writing equations, using counting chips, developing their own drawings) to represent addition and subtraction situations. When children **model with mathematics** in such ways, they are building capacity for deeper and meaningful understanding.

Professional Development Videos:
Addition and Subtraction with Regrouping, Grades K–2, Segment 3

Daily Classroom Management

Differentiated Instruction

Whole Group	Small Group	Whole Group
1 ENGAGE **2** EXPLORE	**3** EXPLAIN ✓ QUICK CHECK	**4** ELABORATE **5** EVALUATE

0 to 1 correct ▲ RtI

INTERVENE
These children need lesson support.

2 correct

ON LEVEL
These children are ready to begin independent practice.

Advanced

ENRICH
These children are ready for enrichment.

Extra Support

Teachers may need to decelerate the rate at which new material is introduced.

- Reteach (in the *Chapter Resources*)
- **ELL** Activity

GO DIGITAL
- Strategic Intervention Guide
- Intensive Intervention Guide
- Personal Math Trainer

On Level

- Practice and Homework (in the *Student Edition*)
- **ELL** Activity

GO DIGITAL
- HMH Mega Math
- *i*Tools

Enrich

Teachers may need to accelerate the rate at which new material is introduced.

- Advanced Learners Activity
- Enrich (in the *Chapter Resources*)
- Extend the Project
- **ELL** Activity

GO DIGITAL
- HMH Mega Math
- *i*Tools

WHAT ARE THE OTHER CHILDREN DOING?

Grab-and-Go!™
Differentiated Centers Kit

The kit provides literature, games, and activities for use every day.

Strategies for
English Language Learners

The **Understand Context Strategy** encourages teachers to use context to clarify and develop meaning for words and phrases including homophones, idioms, and colloquial expressions.

by Elizabeth Jiménez
CEO, GEMAS Consulting
Professional Expert on
English Learner Education
Bilingual Education and Dual Language
Pomona, California

Benefit to English Language Learners

Teaching children mathematical words and phrases in context eliminates confusion and helps build understanding of the concepts. The Understand Context strategy is beneficial to English Language Learners because:

- it recognizes that some words and phrases may be confusing and proactively addresses these words and phrases within the lesson.

- it respects the learner's need for explicit instruction of words that may seem commonplace to the native English speaker.

- it reduces anxiety as it seeks to address the needs of the learner.

From the Research

"ELLs initially learn word meanings best through explicit instruction in combination with rich opportunities to listen, observe, participate, and interact."

The Education Alliance Brown, University, The Teacher's Guide to Diversity: Building a Knowledge Base, 2006.

Planning for Instruction

Idioms and colloquial expressions can be difficult for English Language Learners to understand. The language of mathematics is additionally confusing because many words and phrases take on new meaning in a math lesson. For example, you can *count on* your friend, but you also *count on* in math.

Children need to learn the meanings of words and phrases in context through the use of manipulatives, visuals, direct instruction, discussions, and experiential activities. English Language Learners need repeated exposure to new words and phrases in context, and multiple opportunities to use the words.

To help children understand new words and phrases:

- Use familiar synonyms or simple definitions, defining the word in context often.

- Create a chart of phrases associated with a topic. For example, addition phrases might include *how many in all* and *put together*, as well as *sum, plus,* and *addend.*

- Much like the Develop Meaning strategy, Understand Context promotes understanding of concepts through vocabulary development. Use and define words in context to clarify meaning for English Language Learners, who may hesitate to show their confusion.

Linguistic Note

The language in a math textbook can be challenging for English Language Learners. Many mathematics terms have multiple meanings. Taking time to distinguish between the meanings of these terms will help avoid confusion when asking questions such as *How many tens in 34?*

Developing Math Language

Chapter Vocabulary

ones the value of a digit in the ones position on a place value chart

ten a group of ten ones

 Visualize It

Have children make a list of cue words from word problems for each review vocabulary word as they go through the chapter.

Word	
Meaning	
Example	

 • **Interactive Student Edition**
• **Multimedia eGlossary**

ELL Vocabulary Activity

See ELL Activity Guide for leveled activities.

Objective Review the math terms *ones* and *ten*.

Materials Vocabulary Cards for *ones* and *ten* (see *eTeacher Resources*), base-ten blocks

Show children a tens block and explain that it represents 1 ten. Hold up the Vocabulary Cards for *ones* and *ten* and explain that a base-ten block represents 1 ten or 10 ones. Then, place 5 tens on the table. Have children count the tens and tell you the number they represent. 50

Practice vocabulary by having children respond in complete sentences to questions such as:

Beginning
- Which block shows one ten? Have children pick up a tens block and say, "This block shows one ten."

Intermediate
- How many tens do you need to show 50? I need 5 tens to show 50.

Advanced
- How can you show the tens and ones of the number 73 in different ways using base-ten blocks? Explain and give examples. Possible answers: 7 tens, 3 ones; 6 tens 13 ones.

Vocabulary Strategy • Graphic Organizer

Materials **K.I.M. Map** (see *eTeacher Resources*)

- Write the vocabulary word in the left column.
- Information about the word should be written in the center column.
- Have children draw a picture of the vocabulary word as a memory clue in the right column.

K Key Idea	I Information	M Memory Clue
ones		
ten		

Review Prerequisite Skills

TIER 2

Model Addition Facts

Objective Use doubles, doubles plus 1, and doubles minus 1 to add.
Materials connecting cubes, index cards

- Prepare ahead of time index cards that have an assortment of doubles addition problems, doubles plus 1 addition problems, or doubles minus 1 addition problems on each card. Do not include sums.

- Write the terms *doubles, doubles plus 1,* and *double minus 1* on the board. Have volunteers provide an example of each kind of fact, such as $4 + 4 = 8$, $4 + 5 = 9$, and $6 + 5 = 11$, and write them on the board below their respective type.

- Have children work in groups of 4 or 5. Give each child in a group an index card. Have children identify the kind of fact they have. **What addition problem do you have?** Possible answer: $8 + 9$ **Can you find the sum using doubles, doubles plus 1, or doubles minus 1?** Possible answer: I can use doubles plus 1. Children use connecting cubes to model the addition fact.

	8 + 9
3 + 3	7 + 6
2 + 3	9 + 9

- Have group members check each child's addition.

TIER 3

Show Subtraction

Objective Subtract within 10.
Materials connecting cubes, Numeral Cards (0–10) (see *eTeacher Resources*)

- Give each child connecting cubes and a Numeral Card. Have children show that number using connecting cubes.

- **How can you model your number?** Possible answer: I can count out that number of connecting cubes and make a cube train.

- Give each child a Numeral Card with a number less than the first Numeral Card. Have the child remove that many cubes from the cube train. **How does your cube train show subtraction?** Possible answer: I took away cubes from my cube train.

- Work with each child to write a subtraction sentence. Repeat with other pairs of Numeral Cards.

8

$$8 - 3 = 5$$

Number and Operations in Base Ten

Making Content Connections

Across Grades

Before Grade 1, children were introduced to addition and subtraction. Through *taking apart* and *putting together,* children built a strong understanding of the basics of addition and subtraction (K.OA.A). Children also composed and decomposed numbers 11–19 to gain place value foundations for tens and ones using objects and drawings (K.NBT.A).

In Chapter 8, children expand upon their basic knowledge of addition and subtraction. Children learn to add and to subtract multiples of ten using models and place value strategies. This work leads into adding a two-digit number with a one digit-number using a hundred chart, base-ten blocks, and quick pictures. Children can see with quick pictures and a place-value chart how to regroup ones to compose a ten. Then they use these skills to solve addition word problems. Children explain the method and the reasoning they used to solve the problems (1.NBT.C.4). This progresses to children understanding that the relationship between addition and subtraction with larger numbers is the same strategy as with numbers within 20.

After Grade 1, children continue to build fluency in addition and subtraction within 20. This fluency will be applied as children relate place value and properties of operations to addition and subtraction. Children will also add and subtract within 1,000 using strategies based on place value and compose or decompose tens or hundreds (2.NBT.B.7).

Connect to the Major Work

Part of the major work in Grade 1 is to use place-value understanding and properties of operations to add and subtract (1.NBT.C). Children build on their understanding of addition and subtraction to two-digit numbers. Children use models to learn how to compose a ten when using place value strategies to add a one-digit number to a two-digit number. They also explore the relationship between addition and subtraction with two-digit numbers. They continue building fluency with addition and subtraction, while learning the concept of place value and solving word problems.

Common Core State Standards Across the Grades

Before

Domain: Operations and Algebraic Thinking

Cluster A: Understand addition as putting together and adding to, and understand subtraction as taking apart and taking from.
Standards: K.OA.A.1, K.OA.A.2, K.OA.A.3, K.OA.A.4, K.OA.A.5

Domain: Number and Operations in Base Ten

Cluster A: Work with numbers 11–19 to gain foundations for place value.
Standard: K.NBT.A.1

Grade 1

Domain: Operations and Algebraic Thinking

■ **Cluster C:** Add and subtract within 20.
Standard: 1.OA.C.6

Domain: Number and Operations in Base Ten

■ **Cluster C:** Use place value understanding and properties of operations to add and subtract.
Standards: 1.NBT.C.4, 1.NBT.C.6

After

Domain: Operations and Algebraic Thinking

Cluster B: Add and subtract within 20.
Standard: 2.OA.B.2

Domain: Number and Operations in Base Ten

Cluster B: Use place value understanding and properties of operations to add and subtract.
Standards: 2.NBT.B.5, 2.NBT.B.6, 2.NBT.B.7, 2.NBT.B.8, 2.NBT.B.9

For the full text of the Common Core State Standards, see the A page of each lesson or the *Common Core State Standards Correlations* in the *Planning Guide.*
For the full text of the Standards for Mathematical Practices, see *Mathematical Practices in GO Math!* in the *Planning Guide.*

Chapter 8

Introduce the Chapter

Curious About Math with Curious George

There are 4 boxes of oranges on a table. Each box holds 10 oranges. How many oranges are there? 40 oranges

Additional facts about oranges:

- Almost all oranges are harvested by hand.
- An orange continues to ripen after it is picked.

Discussion Questions

- **What are some ways you can use an orange?** Possible answers: eat it, squeeze it for juice, put it in salads

- **What are some parts of an orange?** peel, rind, pulp, seeds, sections

Chapter 8
Two-Digit Addition and Subtraction

Curious About Math with Curious George

There are 4 boxes of oranges on a table. Each box holds 10 oranges. How many oranges are there?

Chapter 8   four hundred thirty-three **433**

Intervention Options  **RtI** Response to Intervention

Use Show What You Know, Lesson Quick Check, and Assessments to diagnose children's intervention levels.

TIER 1	**TIER 2**	**TIER 3**	**ENRICHMENT**
On-Level Intervention	**Strategic Intervention**	**Intensive Intervention**	**Independent Activities**
For children who are generally at grade level but need early intervention with the lesson concepts, use:	For children who need small group instruction to review concepts and skills needed for the chapter, use:	For children who need one-on-one instruction to build foundational skills for the chapter, use:	For children who successfully complete lessons, use:

TIER 1
- Reteach (in the *Chapter Resources*)
- Personal Math Trainer
- Tier 1 Activity online

TIER 2
- Strategic Intervention Guide
- Personal Math Trainer
- Prerequisite Skills Activities
- Tier 2 Activity online

TIER 3
- Intensive Intervention Guide
- Personal Math Trainer
- Prerequisite Skills Activities

ENRICHMENT

Differentiated Centers Kit
- Advanced Learners Activity for every lesson
- Enrich Activity (in the *Chapter Resources*)
- HMH Mega Math

Name _____

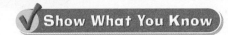 **Show What You Know**

 **Personal Math Trainer**
Online Assessment
and Intervention

Add and Subtract

Use ■ and �■ to add. Write the sum.
Break apart �■ to subtract.
Write the difference. (K.OA.A.1)

1.

$4 + 1 = \underline{5}$

$5 - 1 = \underline{4}$

Count Groups to 20

Circle groups of 10. Write how many. (1.NBT.A.1) Children's circling may vary.

2.
⭐⭐⭐⭐⭐ ⭐⭐⭐⭐⭐
⭐⭐⭐⭐⭐ ⭐⭐⭐⭐
14

3. 
⭐⭐
⭐⭐
⭐⭐
⭐⭐
⭐⭐
⭐⭐
12

Use a Hundred Chart to Count

Touch and count. Shade the last
number counted. (1.NBT.A.1)

1	2	3	4	5	6	7	8	9	10
11	12	13	14	15	16	17	18	19	20
21	22	23	24	25	26	27	28	29	30
31	32	33	34	35	36	37	38	39	40
41	42	43	44	45	46	47	48	49	50
51	52	53	54	55	56	57	58	59	60
61	62	63	64	65	66	67	68	69	70
71	72	73	74	75	76	77	78	79	80
81	82	83	84	85	86	87	88	89	90
91	92	93	94	95	96	97	98	99	100

4. Start at 1 and count to 20.
5. Start at 30 and count to 56.
6. Start at 77 and count to 93.

This page checks understanding of important skills needed
for success in Chapter 8.

434 four hundred thirty-four

© Houghton Mifflin Harcourt Publishing Company

Assessing Prior Knowledge

Have children complete on their own **Show What You Know.** Tested items are the prerequisite skills of this chapter.

Diagnostic Interview Task

The alternative interview tasks below evaluate children's understanding of each **Show What You Know** skill. The diagnostic chart may be used for intervention on prerequisite skills.

For evaluation checklist see *Chapter Resource Book.*

Materials two-color counters, Workmat 8 (see *eTeacher Resources*)

- Have the child use counters to show 3 + 2. Ask the child to name the sum of 3 + 2. Then have the child use the counters to show 5 − 2. Ask the child to name the difference for 5 − 2. Check children's work.

- Have the child draw counters on Workmat 8 to show 14. Have the child draw a circle around the group of ten and then write how many counters there are in all. 14

- Display a Hundred Chart. Ask the child if they will say 20 when counting from 11 to 18. No.

✔ Show What You Know • Diagnostic Assessment

Use to determine if children need intervention for the chapter's prerequisite skills.

Were children successful with Show What You Know?

If NO...then INTERVENE

If YES...then use INDEPENDENT ACTIVITIES

	Skill	Missed More Than	Personal Math Trainer	Intervene With
TIER 3	Add and Subtract	0	K.OA.A.1	*Intensive Intervention* Skill 38; *Intensive Intervention User Guide* Activity 8
TIER 2	Count Groups to 20	0	1.NBT.A.1	Strategic Intervention Skill 10
TIER 2	Use a Hundred Chart to Count	1	1.NBT.A.1	Strategic Intervention Skill 15

Differentiated Centers Kit

Use the Enrich Activity in the *Chapter Resources* or the independent activities in the *Grab-and-Go™ Differentiated Centers Kit.*

Two-Digit Addition and Subtraction   434

Vocabulary Builder  MATHEMATICAL PRACTICES

Have children complete the activities on this page by working alone or with partners.

▶ **Visualize It** Have children sort the review words and record them in the graphic organizer. Have children share how they sorted the words and tell how they decided where to place each one.

▶ **Understand Vocabulary**

You may want to share the following with children.

1. You can **add** to find how many in a group.

2. You can **subtract** to find how many are left.

3. You can find the **sum** for 8 + 7.

4. You can find the **difference** for 8 − 7.

Name _____

Vocabulary Builder

Visualize It
Sort the review words from the box.

Put Together

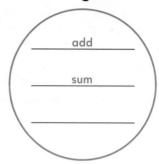

add

sum

_____

Take Apart

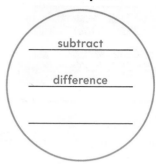

subtract

difference

_____

Understand Vocabulary
Use a review word to complete each sentence.

1. 8 is the ___difference___ for 17 − 9.

2. 17 is the ___sum___ for 8 + 9.

3. When you ___add___ 4 to 8, you find the sum.

4. When you ___subtract___ 4 from 8, you find the difference.

Chapter 8

 • Interactive Student Edition
• Multimedia eGlossary

four hundred thirty-five **435**

Vocabulary Cards

Children can enhance their understanding of **key chapter vocabulary** through the use of the vocabulary cards found in the Student Edition.

Have children cut out the cards and create their own deck of terms. You can use these cards to **reinforce knowledge** and **reading across the content areas.**

Game Neighborhood Sums

Materials

  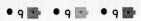

Play with a partner.

1. Put your 🎎 on START.
2. Spin the 🕐. Move that number of spaces.
3. Make a ten to help you find the sum.
4. The other player uses 🎲 🎲 🎲 to check.
5. If you are not correct, you lose a turn.
6. The first player to get to END wins.

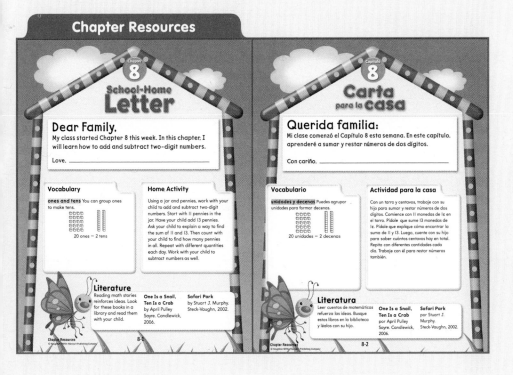

2 4 +8 ‾‾ 14	Move ahead one space.	4 9 +6 ‾‾ 19	4 4 +6 ‾‾ 14	9 1 +6 ‾‾ 16
				END

4
6
+3
‾‾
13 | 5
3
+7
‾‾
15 | 9
7
+1
‾‾
17 | Move back one space. | 3
7
+7
‾‾
17 | 5
8
+5
‾‾
18

6
6
+4
‾‾
16

START | 2
4
+8
‾‾
14 | Move ahead one space. | 6
1
+9
‾‾
16 | 8
8
+2
‾‾
18

Game Neighborhood Sums

▶ Using the Game

Set up a game center in the classroom. Include the Neighborhood Sums game along with the materials needed to play. Have children visit the center with a partner to play the game.

Materials red and blue game pieces, red, blue, and orange connecting cubes (9 of each), 3-section spinner (labeled 1–3) (see *eTeacher Resources*), paper clip, pencil

- If partners have difficulty with the mental math, you might suggest they write the number sentences on their MathBoard to help them find the sum.

- Encourage children to identify the numbers they use to make ten.

- After children have played the game you may wish to have them take it home to play for practice. Playing the game at home will continually reinforce the basic facts and build fluency.

Chapter Resources

School-Home Letter available in English and Spanish in the *Chapter Resources*. Multiple languages available online at *www.thinkcentral.com*.

The letter provides families with an overview of the math in the chapter, math vocabulary, an activity, and literature to read together.

Chapter 8 — School-Home Letter

Dear Family,
My class started Chapter 8 this week. In this chapter, I will learn how to add and subtract two-digit numbers.

Love, _____

Vocabulary
ones and tens You can group ones to make tens.

20 ones = 2 tens

Home Activity
Using a jar and pennies, work with your child to add and subtract two-digit numbers. Start with 11 pennies in the jar. Have your child add 13 pennies. Ask your child to explain a way to find the sum of 11 and 13. Then count with your child to find how many pennies in all. Repeat with different quantities each day. Work with your child to subtract numbers as well.

Literature
Reading math stories reinforces ideas. Look for these books in a library and read them with your child.

One Is a Snail, Ten Is a Crab by April Pulley Sayre. Candlewick, 2006.

Safari Park by Stuart J. Murphy. Steck-Vaughn, 2002.

Capítulo 8 — Carta para la casa

Querida familia:
Mi clase comenzó el Capítulo 8 esta semana. En este capítulo, aprenderé a sumar y restar números de dos dígitos.

Con cariño, _____

Vocabulario
unidades y decenas Puedes agrupar unidades para formar decenas.

20 unidades = 2 decenas

Actividad para la casa
Con un tarro y centavos, trabaje con su hijo para sumar y restar números de dos dígitos. Comience con 11 monedas de 1¢ en el tarro. Pídale que sume 13 monedas de 1¢. Pídale que explique cómo encontrar la suma de 11 y 13. Luego, cuente con su hijo para saber cuántos centavos hay en total. Repita con diferentes cantidades cada día. Trabaje con él para restar números también.

Literatura
Leer cuentos de matemáticas refuerza las ideas. Busque estos libros en la biblioteca y léalos con su hijo.

One Is a Snail, Ten Is a Crab por April Pulley Sayre. Candlewick, 2006.

Safari Park por Stuart J. Murphy. Steck-Vaughn, 2002.

Going Places with *GO Math!* Words

Introduce the Words

Provide child-friendly explanations of chapter vocabulary. Ask volunteers to explain the math term in their own words.

- **17 + 20 = 37** is an *addition sentence*.
- When you subtract one number from another number, you find the *difference*.
- When you *subtract*, you take away.
- **50 – 30 = 20** is a *subtraction sentence*.
- When you add two or more numbers, you find the *sum*.

Math Journal  Math

Have children draw pictures or use numbers to show what each term means. Then ask them to discuss their work with a partner.

Bingo:

Play the Game

The game may be played before, during, or after the content is taught. Read the game directions with children, and explain how to use the bingo boards in the Student Book.

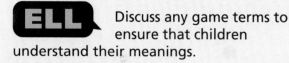

Play one round of the game as a class. Take on the role of the caller. Choose a Vocabulary Card, read the word aloud, and have children put a game marker in each box that has that word. Repeat this procedure until a child has marked three boxes in a line going across or down. Model how to check the child's answers against the words read aloud.

The directions for playing the game can also be found in the Chapter Resource book.

ELL Discuss any game terms to ensure that children understand their meanings.

Bingo

Materials
- 1 set of word cards
- 18 ●

How to Play
Play with a partner.
1. Mix the cards. Put the cards in a pile with the blank side up.
2. Take a card. Read the word.
3. Find the matching word on your bingo board. Cover the word with a ●. Put the card at the bottom of the pile.
4. The other player takes a turn.
5. The first player to cover 3 spaces in a line wins. The line may go across or down.

Word Box
add
addition
  sentence
difference
fewer
more
subtract
subtraction
  sentence
sum

Player 1

fewer	add	more
addition sentence	**BINGO**	sum
subtraction sentence	difference	subtract

Player 2

subtraction sentence	addition sentence	fewer
add	**BINGO**	difference
subtract	more	sum

© Houghton Mifflin Harcourt Publishing Company

Chapter 8 four hundred thirty-six **436A**

Journal

The Write Way

Reflect

Choose one idea. Draw and write about it.

- Write sentences that include at least two of these terms.

  add   subtract   addition sentence   subtraction sentence

- Explain how you would solve this problem.

$$53 + 20 = \underline{\qquad}$$

What You Need

Each pair of players needs one set of the Vocabulary Cards in the Student Edition.

The Write Way

These short, informal writing activities address the vocabulary and content from this chapter. Communicating about math clarifies and deepens children's understandings about math concepts.

Read the writing prompts with children. Give them 5–10 minutes to choose an idea and write about it.

When children have completed their first drafts, share and discuss the following questions. Then provide children with additional time to use the questions to review and revise their writing.

- **Does my writing show that I understand the math idea(s)?**
- **Do I use math words correctly?**
- **Is my writing clear and easy to follow?**
- **Do I use complete sentences? Have I checked to be sure my grammar, spelling, and punctuation are correct?**

Ask volunteers to share their finished writing with a partner or the class. Encourage discussion of different ways children may have addressed each prompt. Point out that often there is not just one correct answer.

ELL Have children use the Vocabulary Cards in the Student Edition as a reference for word meanings. Guide them to use the lessons and example problems in the Student Edition if they need additional support.

Add and Subtract Within 20

LESSON AT A GLANCE

F C R Focus:

Common Core State Standards

1.OA.C.6 Add and subtract within 20, demonstrating fluency for addition and subtraction within 10. Use strategies such as counting on; making ten (e.g., $8 + 6 = 8 + 2 + 4 = 10 + 4 = 14$); decomposing a number leading to a ten (e.g., $13 - 4 = 13 - 3 - 1 = 10 - 1 = 9$); using the relationship between addition and subtraction (e.g., knowing that $8 + 4 + 12$, one knows $12 - 8 = 4$); and creating equivalent but easier or known sums (e.g., adding $6 + 7$ by creating the known equivalent $6 + 6 + 1 = 12 + 1 = 13$).

MATHEMATICAL PRACTICES (See *Mathematical Practices in GO Math!* in the *Planning Guide* for full text.)
MP1 Make sense of problems and persevere in solving them. **MP3** Construct viable arguments and critique the reasoning of others. **MP6** Attend to precision.

F C R Coherence:

Standards Across the Grades

Before	Grade 1	After
K.OA.A.2	1.OA.C.6	2.OA.B.2
K.NBT.A.1		

F C R Rigor:

Level 1: Understand Concepts...................*Share and Show* (✓ Checked Items)
Level 2: Procedural Skills and Fluency.......*On Your Own, Practice and Homework*
Level 3: Applications.................................*Think Smarter and Go Deeper*

Learning Objective
Add and subtract within 20.

Language Objective
Children exchange ideas with a partner about what strategies you can use to add and subtract.

Materials
MathBoard, connecting cubes, two-color counters, Workmat 8 (see *eTeacher Resources*)

F C R For more about how *GO Math!* fosters **Coherence** within the Content Standards and Mathematical Progressions for this chapter, see page 433J.

About the Math
Professional Development

Progress to Algebra
Why Teach This

Children have learned several strategies for adding and subtracting. These strategies build on the properties of operations or on the inverse relationship of addition and subtraction.

Understanding how and why these strategies work is key for children to add and subtract fluently. It is important for children to achieve fluency with facts to be successful in later work with multi-digit addition and subtraction.

Children choose and use a strategy to solve addition and subtraction problems and then explain how they found the answers. Help children understand that in many cases problems can be solved successfully with any of several strategies. Emphasize that children may use any strategy they find easy or effective.

 Professional Development Videos

SE Interactive Student Edition

Personal Math Trainer

Math on the Spot Video

*i*T *i*Tools: Counters

MM HMH Mega Math

Daily Routines
Common Core

 Problem of the Day 8.1

Basic Facts Write two related subtraction facts for $9 + 3 = 12$.

$12 - 3 = 9$ and $12 - 9 = 3$

Continue with other facts.

Vocabulary

GO DIGITAL
- Interactive Student Edition
- Multimedia eGlossary

Fluency Builder
Number Sentence Stories

| Common Core Fluency |
| Standard 1.OA.C.6 |

Materials Addition and Subtraction Sentences to 20, Math Mountain Cards (See *eTeacher Resources*)

Have children work in pairs. Give each pair several addition and several subtraction sentences. Have children place the cards face down in a pile.

Have one partner select a number sentence, show the sentence, and say the number sentence. Have the other partner make up a story that uses the numbers in the number sentence. If the partners agree that the story matches the number sentence, have them leave that number sentence face up.

Repeat the activity by having partners switch roles.

If time allows, have one partner select a number sentence and then say related number sentences. For example, if the number sentence is $8 - 5 = 3$, a related sentence would be $8 - 3 = 5$.

Pages 120–121 in *Strategies and Practice for Skills and Facts Fluency* provide additional fluency support for this lesson.

① ENGAGE

with the Interactive Student Edition

Essential Question

What strategies can you use to add and subtract?

Making Connections

Ask children to tell what they know about addition strategies.

- **What addition strategy might you use to add 7 + 2?** Count on
- **What addition strategy might you use to add 8 + 4?** Make a ten
- **What addition strategy might you use to add 6 + 7?** Add doubles plus 1

Learning Activity

What problem are children trying to solve? Connect the story to the problem. Ask the following questions.

- **How can you model the strategy "make a ten" for the addition fact 9 + 4?** I can make a nine cube train and a 4 cube train. Then I can move 1 cube over to make a ten. I can see I have $10 + 3$ or 13. So I know that $9 + 4$ is 13.

- **How does a model help you know what strategy to use?** A model helps me see patterns.

Literacy and Mathematics

Choose from one or more of the following activities.

- Have children name a number fact and the strategy they would use to solve that number fact.

- Have children create number stories about the objects in the picture. Have other children share the strategies they would use to solve the number stories.

② EXPLORE

Listen and Draw (Real World)

Materials connecting cubes, two-color counters, Workmat 8 (see *eTeacher Resources*)

In this lesson, children review what they have learned about addition and subtraction to prepare them for performing these operations with two-digit numbers.

Read the following aloud.

Choose and model a strategy to solve the addition fact. Then draw to show your work.

- **Which objects did you use to model the addition? Why?** Possible answer: I used cubes because I can show one addend in one color cube train and the other addend in a different color cube train.

- **What did you draw to show your work?** Possible answer: I drew a 5-cube train and another 5-cube train. Then I crossed out one cube to show 4.

 MP3 Construct viable arguments and critique the reasoning of others. Use **Math Talk** to focus on children's understanding of strategies for adding and subtracting within 20.

- **How did you decide which strategy to use?** Possible answer: I look at the numbers to see if I can easily make a ten, use a doubles facts, or use a basic fact to solve the problem, then I use that strategy.

 Strategy:
Scaffold Language

Have children choose a strategy to solve addition and subtraction problems. Write a chart like the one shown for children to see.

Review each strategy. Emphasize that there is more than one way to solve a problem.

Have children explain how to use a strategy to solve a problem.

Addition Strategies	Subtraction Strategies
counting on	counting back
making ten	subtract to make ten
doubles	thinking about addition
doubles plus one	related facts
doubles minus one	

Progress to Algebra **1.OA.C.6** Add and subtract within 20, demonstrating fluency for addition and subtraction within 10. Use strategies such as counting on; making ten (e.g., $8 + 6 = 8 + 2 + 4 = 10 + 4 = 14$); decomposing a number leading to a ten (e.g., $13 - 4 = 13 - 3 - 1 = 10 - 1 = 9$); using the relationship between addition and subtraction (e.g., knowing that $8 + 4 = 12$, one knows $12 - 8 = 4$); and creating equivalent but easier or known sums (e.g., adding $6 + 7$ by creating the known equivalent $6 + 6 + 1 = 12 + 1 = 13$).

Name _____

Add and Subtract Within 20

Essential Question What strategies can you use to add and subtract?

Common Core — Operations and Algebraic Thinking—1.OA.C.6

MATHEMATICAL PRACTICES
MP1, MP3, MP6

Listen and Draw (Real World)

What is $5 + 4$?
Use a strategy to solve the addition fact. Draw to show your work.

Possible drawing shown.

$5 + 4 = \underline{9}$

Math Talk: Possible answer: I used the strategy doubles minus one. First I used connecting cubes to model the doubles fact $5 + 5 = 10$. Then I took one cube away to show $5 + 4 = 9$.

FOR THE TEACHER • Have children choose and model a strategy to solve the addition fact. Then have them draw to show their work.

MATHEMATICAL PRACTICES 3

Apply What strategy did you use to find the answer?

Chapter 8   four hundred thirty-seven **437**

© Houghton Mifflin Harcourt Publishing Company

Reateach 8.1 ▲RtI

Name _____   Lesson 8.1 Reteach

Add and Subtract Within 20

You can use strategies to add or subtract.

- count on
- doubles
- doubles plus one
- count back
- related facts
- doubles minus one

What is $5 + 6$?   I can use doubles plus one.

$5 + 5 = 10$

So, $5 + 6 = \underline{11}$.

What is $12 - 4$?   I can use a related fact.

$8 + 4 = 12$

So, $12 - 4 = \underline{8}$.

Add or subtract.

1. $12 - 3 = \underline{9}$	2. $8 + 9 = \underline{17}$
3. $10 - 5 = \underline{5}$	4. $13 - 7 = \underline{6}$
5. $7 + 8 = \underline{15}$	6. $6 + 6 = \underline{12}$

Chapter Resources   8-5   Reteach
© Houghton Mifflin Harcourt Publishing Company

Enrich 8.1   Differentiated Instruction

Name _____   Lesson 8.1 Enrich

Good Strategy!

Write any number from 3 to 9 in the box. Choose a strategy to help you find the sum or difference. Then write the strategy you used. Try to use each strategy.

Check children's work.

Strategies I know
- count on
- count back
- doubles plus one
- doubles minus one
- make a ten
- use a related fact

1. $11 - \boxed{} = $ ____ Strategy: ____	2. $6 + \boxed{} = $ ____ Strategy: ____
3. $8 + \boxed{} = $ ____ Strategy: ____	4. $12 - \boxed{} = $ ____ Strategy: ____
5. $9 - \boxed{} = $ ____ Strategy: ____	6. $7 + \boxed{} = $ ____ Strategy: ____

Writing and Reasoning For Exercise 4, explain why you chose the strategy you used.

Possible answer: I used a related fact because counting back would take longer.

Chapter Resources   8-6   Enrich
© Houghton Mifflin Harcourt Publishing Company

Model and Draw

Think of a strategy you can use to add or subtract.

What is 14 − 6?

I can use a related fact.

_6_ ⊕ _8_ = 14

So, 14 − 6 = _8_.

Share and Show MATH BOARD

Add or subtract.

1. 5 + 3 = _8_   2. 10 − 5 = _5_   3. 3 + 6 = _9_

4. 12 − 5 = _7_   5. 15 − 9 = _6_   6. 5 + 7 = _12_

7. 8 + 7 = _15_   8. 9 − 7 = _2_   9. 5 + 5 = _10_

10. 12 − 7 = _5_   11. 18 − 9 = _9_   12. 9 + 4 = _13_

13. 2 + 7 = _9_   14. 5 − 1 = _4_   15. 9 + 1 = _10_

16. 7 − 6 = _1_   ⊘17. 13 − 4 = _9_   ⊘18. 2 + 6 = _8_

438 four hundred thirty-eight

Advanced Learners 🕐 Logical / Mathematical Partners

Materials connecting cubes, paper and pencil

- Write 8 + 3 + 5 = _____ on the board.

- Challenge partners to use this number sentence to show the six ways they can add in different orders.

- Have one partner model the way to add the numbers. The other partner writes the corresponding number sentence.

- Next, have partners switch roles to find a second way to order the addends.

- Have partners continue in this way until they find all six ways to order the three addends.

---

③ EXPLAIN

Model and Draw  Common Core MATHEMATICAL PRACTICES

MP1 Make sense of problems and persevere in solving them. Work through the model with children. Have them answer the first question and trace the numbers as they answer the other questions.

- **Which number in the subtraction fact is the sum in the related addition fact?** 14
- **Which number is an addend in the related addition fact for 14 − 6?** 6
- **6 plus which number equals 14?** 8
- **What is another way to find the difference? Explain.** Possible answer: I can draw 14 circles. Then I circle 6 circles and cross out the group. I count how many are left.

Share and Show   MATH BOARD

Have children write the sums and differences. Note their fluency with these facts. Children may use their MathBoards to make their drawings if they need to.

- **How do you know your answer to Exercise 18 is correct?** Possible answer: I used the strategy count on to find the answer.

Use the checked exercises for **Quick Check.**

✔️ **Quick Check**   RtI

If	a child misses the checked exercises
Then	**Differentiate Instruction** with

- Reteach 8.1
- Personal Math Trainer 1.OA.C.6
- RtI Tier 1 Activity (online)

⚠️ **COMMON ERRORS**

Error Children confuse operation symbols.

Example For Exercise 3, children may subtract 3 from 6 and write 3 instead of adding 3 and 6.

Springboard to Learning As children become more fluent with facts, they may read a fact too quickly and perform the wrong operation. Suggest that they circle the symbol before calculating.

Lesson 8.1 438

© Houghton Mifflin Harcourt Publishing Company

On Your Own

MP6 Attend to precision. If children answered Exercises 17 and 18 correctly, assign Exercises 19–43.

Point out that the addition and subtraction facts in Exercises 19–42 are written in vertical form.

THINK SMARTER

MP3 Construct viable arguments and critique the reasoning of others. Exercise 43 requires children to use higher order thinking skills as they apply what they know about addition and subtraction facts. Children need to identify the missing number as one of the addends to write the fact. Encourage children to think of a related subtraction fact.

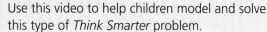

Math on the Spot Video Tutor

Use this video to help children model and solve this type of *Think Smarter* problem.

Math on the Spot videos are in the Interactive Student Edition and at *www.thinkcentral.com*.

GO DEEPER

MP6 Attend to precision. To extend their thinking, ask children the following question to help them apply their understanding of the properties of addition.

- **Could Jamal be thinking of a different addition fact? Explain.** Possible answer: Yes. You can add two numbers in any order and still get the same sum. So, you can switch the order of addends.

MP1 Make sense of problems and persevere in solving them.

- **How would the number sentence change if Jamal was using the same numbers but he was thinking of a subtraction fact?** Possible answer: He could be thinking of 15 − 8 = 7 or 15 − 7 = 8.

Name _____

On Your Own

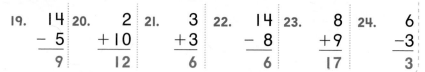

MATHEMATICAL PRACTICE 3 **Apply** Add or subtract.

19.	20.	21.	22.	23.	24.
14 − 5 = 9	2 + 10 = 12	3 + 3 = 6	14 − 8 = 6	8 + 9 = 17	6 − 3 = 3

25.	26.	27.	28.	29.	30.
6 − 5 = 1	2 + 8 = 10	0 + 5 = 5	10 − 2 = 8	9 + 9 = 18	5 − 4 = 1

31.	32.	33.	34.	35.	36.
8 − 8 = 0	10 + 1 = 11	4 + 7 = 11	9 − 3 = 6	1 + 8 = 9	17 − 9 = 8

37.	38.	39.	40.	41.	42.
13 − 7 = 6	6 + 5 = 11	10 + 2 = 12	14 − 9 = 5	10 + 10 = 20	11 − 3 = 8

43. **THINK SMARTER** Jamal thinks of an addition fact. The sum is 15. One addend is 8. What is a fact Jamal could be thinking of?

$$\underline{8} \;\oplus\; \underline{7} \;=\; \underline{15}$$

or 7 + 8 = 15

Chapter 8 • Lesson 1   four hundred thirty-nine **439**

PROBLEM TYPE SITUATIONS

Addition and Subtraction

Add To • Change Unknown
Exercise: 44

Put Together/Take Apart • Addend Unknown
Exercise: 43

Problem Solving • Applications   WRITE Math

Solve. Write or draw to explain.

44. *THINK SMARTER* There are 9 ants on a rock. Some more ants get on the rock. Now there are 18 ants on the rock. How many more ants got on the rock?

__9__ more ants

45. *GO DEEPER* Fill in the blanks. Write a number sentence to solve.

Answers will vary. Possible answers shown.

Lin sees __8__ bees. Some bees flew away. Now there are __3__ bees. How many bees flew away?

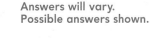

$8 \bigcirc{-} \; 5 \; \bigcirc{=} \; 3$

__5__ bees

46. *THINK SMARTER* Write each addition or subtraction problem in the box below the sum or difference.

7 + 9   6 + 1   17 − 8   14 − 7   8 + 8

7	9	16
6 + 1	17 − 8	7 + 9
14 − 7		8 + 8

 TAKE HOME ACTIVITY • Have your child tell a strategy he or she would use to solve 4 + 8.

440 four hundred forty

© Houghton Mifflin Harcourt Publishing Company • Image Credits: (b) ©Shutterstock; (t) ©Domiciano Pablo Romero Franco/Alamy

---

DIFFERENTIATED INSTRUCTION   INDEPENDENT ACTIVITIES

Differentiated Centers Kit

Activities
Add With Ten

Children complete blue Activity Card 16 by reviewing adding with 10.

Literature
Garden Party

Children read the book and subtract the number of vegetables eaten by the caterpillars.

Games
Neighborhood Sums

Children practice and review sums to 20.

Problem Solving • Applications Real World

You may wish to provide children with connecting cubes or counters for modeling.

GO DEEPER **Multi-Step**

MP1 Make sense of problems and persevere in solving them. In Exercise 45, children first must choose numbers that make sense to complete the *Take From/Change Unknown* problem. The first number must be greater than the second number. Next, children write a number sentence to find the answer.

THINK SMARTER

Exercise 46 assesses whether children can add and subtract fluently within 20. Children sort addition and subtraction expressions by common solutions that are given in a chart. Incorrect answers may result if children do not pay attention to the operation in each expression. Help children who demonstrate calculation errors by reminding them of strategies such as using doubles or making a ten.

⑤ EVALUATE Formative Assessment

Essential Question

Reflect Using the Language Objective Have children exchange ideas with a partner to answer the Essential Question.

What strategies can you use to add and subtract? Possible answers: I can use related facts; I can think about doubles; I can draw pictures or use models such as counters or connecting cubes.

Math Journal  WRITE Math

Write an addition and subtraction fact. Then write a strategy you could use to solve the fact.

Practice and Homework

Use the Practice and Homework pages to provide children with more practice of the concepts and skills presented in this lesson. Children master their understanding as they complete practice items and then challenge their critical thinking skills with Problem Solving. Use the Write Math section to determine children's understanding of content for this lesson. Encourage children to use their Math Journals to record their answers.

Name _____

Add and Subtract Within 20

Common Core **COMMON CORE STANDARD—1.OA.C.6**
Add and subtract within 20.

Add or subtract.

1. 6 $+0$ $\overline{6}$	2. 11 -2 $\overline{9}$	3. 4 $+5$ $\overline{9}$	4. 9 $+8$ $\overline{17}$	5. 4 $+10$ $\overline{14}$	6. 14 -9 $\overline{5}$
7. 7 $+4$ $\overline{11}$	8. 8 -5 $\overline{3}$	9. 10 -10 $\overline{0}$	10. 6 $+7$ $\overline{13}$	11. 18 -9 $\overline{9}$	12. 15 -6 $\overline{9}$

Problem Solving (Real World)

Solve. Draw or write to explain.   Check children's work.

13. Jesse has 4 shells. He finds some more. Now he has 12 shells. How many more shells did Jesse find?

$$12 - 4 = 8$$ ___8___ more shells

14. **WRITE Math** Write an addition or subtraction fact. Then write a strategy you could use to add or subtract.

Check children's work.

_____

_____

_____

© Houghton Mifflin Harcourt Publishing Company

Extend the Math   Activity

Model Strategies

Materials paper, crayons

Investigate Have children choose a fact on the page and draw a model to show a way they would find the sum or difference. Have children share their pictures with the class.

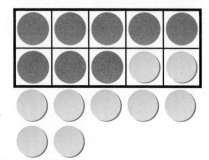

Math Talk Ask questions to help children construct viable arguments for their choices.

- **Which fact did you model? Why?** Possible answer: I chose 8 + 9 as my fact because I can make a ten to help me add.

- **How does your model show the strategy?** Possible answer: I put 8 red counters in a ten frame to show 8. I put 2 yellow counters in the empty spaces to make ten. I know 2 + 7 = 9, so I put 7 more yellow counters under the ten frame. 10 + 7 = 17, so 8 + 9 = 17.

Summarize Have children decide which models work well to show the chosen facts and strategies. As children critique one another, monitor for respectful, thoughtful dialogue.

Lesson Check (1.OA.C.6)

I. What is the sum?
Write the number.

$$8 + 5 = \underline{13}$$

2. What is the difference?
Write the number.

$$11 - 4 = \underline{7}$$

Spiral Review (1.NBT.B.3)

3.

Circle the greater number.	Did tens or ones help you decide?	Write the numbers.
43 (46)	tens (ones)	$\underline{46}$ is greater than $\underline{43}$. $\underline{46} > \underline{43}$

4.

Circle the number that is less.	Did tens or ones help you decide?	Write the numbers.
(69) 84	(tens) ones	$\underline{69}$ is less than $\underline{84}$. $\underline{69} < \underline{84}$

FOR MORE PRACTICE
GO TO THE
Personal Math Trainer

442 four hundred forty-two

© Houghton Mifflin Harcourt Publishing Company

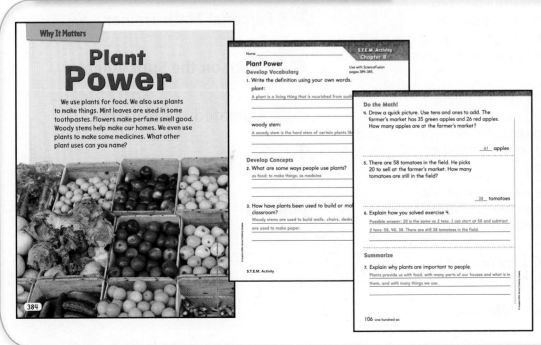

Why It Matters

Plant Power

We use plants for food. We also use plants to make things. Mint leaves are used in some toothpastes. Flowers make perfume smell good. Woody stems help make our homes. We even use plants to make some medicines. What other plant uses can you name?

384

In Chapter 8, children develop their understanding of two-digit addition and subtraction by adding tens and ones. These same topics are used often in the development of various science concepts and process skills.

Children can make the connection between math, science, and technology through the S.T.E.M. activities and activity worksheets found at www.thinkcentral.com. In Chapter 8, children connect math, science, and technology with the S.T.E.M. Activity *Plant Power* and the accompanying worksheets (pages 105 and 106).

Through this S.T.E.M. Activity, children will connect the *GO Math!* Chapter 8 concepts and skills with various definitions of plants and plant parts including modeling and explaining a solution. It is recommended that this S.T.E.M. Activity be used after Lesson 8.7.

Hands On • Add Tens

LESSON AT A GLANCE

F C R Focus:

Common Core State Standards

1.NBT.C.4 Add within 100, including adding a two-digit number and a one-digit number, and adding a two-digit number and a multiple of 10, using concrete models or drawings and strategies based on place value, properties of operations, and/or the relationship between addition and subtraction; relate the strategy to a written method and explain the reasoning used. Understand that in adding two-digit numbers, one adds tens and tens, ones and ones; and sometimes it is necessary to compose a ten.

MATHEMATICAL PRACTICES (See *Mathematical Practices in GO Math!* in the *Planning Guide* for full text.)
MP2 Reason abstractly and quantitatively. **MP7** Look for and make use of structure.

F C R Coherence:

Standards Across the Grades
Before	Grade 1	After
K.NBT.A.1	1.NBT.C.4	2.NBT.B.5

F C R Rigor:

Level 1: Understand Concepts.................*Share and Show* (✓ Checked Items)
Level 2: Procedural Skills and Fluency.......*On Your Own, Practice and Homework*
Level 3: Applications................................*Think Smarter and Go Deeper*

Learning Objective
Draw a model to add tens.

Language Objective
Children model and explain to a partner how you can add tens.

Materials
MathBoard, base-ten blocks, connecting cubes, Workmats 4 and 8 (see *eTeacher Resources*)

F C R For more about how *GO Math!* fosters **Coherence** within the Content Standards and Mathematical Progressions for this chapter, see page 433J.

About the Math
Professional Development

Progress to Algebra
Teaching for Depth

As children begin adding tens, some may still need to use cubes or base-ten blocks to show the tens before drawing quick pictures. If children have difficulty making a transition to quick pictures, then they can trace the objects to make their drawings.

Some children may be able to add tens in their heads using addition strategies. These strategies would most likely extend the basic facts to adding tens. A child with strong mental math ability is able to flexibly compose numbers for use in different situations.

Encourage children to develop their own strategies for adding tens. Allow children to describe their strategies, even error-filled ones, without being interrupted or corrected. Children often discover their own mistakes if allowed to think through their idea as they present it, resulting in a deeper understanding for all.

 Professional Development Videos

SE Interactive Student Edition

Personal Math Trainer

Math on the Spot Math on the Spot Video

 Animated Math Models

*i*T *i*Tools: Base-Ten Blocks

 HMH Mega Math

Daily Routines
Common Core

 Problem of the Day 8.2

Basic Facts Add or subtract.

1. $3 + 7 =$ ___10___   3. $13 - 9 =$ ___4___

2. $11 - 6 =$ ___5___   4. $4 + 8 =$ ___12___

Remind children to check their work.

Vocabulary

> **GO DIGITAL** • Interactive Student Edition
> • Multimedia eGlossary

Vocabulary Builder
Addends and Sums

> **Common Core Fluency Standard** 1.OA.C.6

Materials Vocabulary Cards addend, sum (see *eTeacher Resources*)

Show Vocabulary Cards *addend* and *sum*. Pronounce and review the words. Present word problems such as the following.

> **Roger has 9 goldfish. He gets 6 more. How many fish does Roger have?**

Write a number sentence for this problem. Ask children to raise one hand when you point to an addend and both hands when you point to the sum. Repeat with other problems.

Literature Connection

From the Grab-and-Go™ Differentiated Centers Kit

Children read the book and add baseball cards.

It's a Homerun!

① ENGAGE

with the Interactive Student Edition

Essential Question
How can you add tens?

Making Connections
Assess prior knowledge of tens by having children tell how many tens and how many ones in a two-digit number.

- **How many tens are in the number 19?** 1 ten
- **How many ones are in the number 19?** 9 ones
- **What is another way to say 19?** 1 ten 9 ones
- **What is another way to say 25?** 2 tens 5 ones

Learning Activity
What problem are children trying to solve? Connect the story to the problem. Ask the following questions.

- **How many times was the disc thrown before it was dropped?** 20
- **How many tens are in 20? 30?** 2; 3
- **How does your model of ten ones look different from your model of one ten?** 10 ones are the same as 10 individual pieces, like ten connecting cubes. But 1 ten is one piece, like one tens-block.

Literacy and Mathematics
Choose from one or more of the following activities.

- Give children a start number, such as 20, and have them count on 5 more tens. Repeat with other start numbers.

- Give partners two-digit numbers and have them take turns deconstructing the two-digit numbers using this frame:

  ___ is the same as ___ tens and ___ ones.

② **EXPLORE**

Listen and Draw

Materials base-ten blocks, connecting cubes, Workmats 4 and 8 (see *eTeacher Resources*)

Have children use base-ten blocks or connecting cubes to model each addend on a workmat.

> *Barb has 20 baseball cards. Ed has 30 baseball cards. How many baseball cards do they have?* 50 baseball cards

After modeling the problem, have children draw a quick picture at the top of the workspace to represent the addition.

- **How did you model the problem?** Possible answer: I put out 2 tens and 3 tens. Then I put the tens together and counted them to find 5 tens, or 50.

- **How does your drawing show how you solved the problem?** Possible answer: I drew 2 lines for 2 tens and 3 lines for 3 tens. Altogether there are 5 lines, or 5 tens.

The concept of 1 ten being the same as 10 ones can be a difficult concept to grasp. Show how to trade 10 ones for 1 ten.

Read the next problem to the class. Have children solve the problem and record their work at the bottom of the workspace.

> *Kyle has 40 baseball cards. Kim has 50 baseball cards. How many baseball cards do they have?* 90 baseball cards

- **How can you solve this problem without models?** Possible answer: I can think 4 tens + 5 tens = 9 tens; 9 tens is the same as 90.

 MP2 Reason abstractly and quantitatively. Use Math Talk to focus on children's understanding of adding two numbers that have tens and no ones.

- **What does the zero in each of the numbers you added mean?** There are no ones.

 Strategy:
Understand Context

Write **3 + 2 = _____**. Show the problem with base-ten blocks.

Then write **30 + 20 = _____**. Show the problem with base-ten blocks.

Explain how to find the sum. **3 tens plus 2 tens equals 5 tens. 30 + 20 = 50.**

- **How is adding 3 and 2 similar to adding 30 and 20? How is it different?** Use the base-ten blocks to show the difference between adding tens and adding ones.

1.NBT.C.4 Add within 100, including adding a two-digit number and a one-digit number, and adding a two-digit number and a multiple of 10, using concrete models or drawings and strategies based on place value, properties of operations, and/or the relationship between addition and subtraction; relate the strategy to a written method and explain the reasoning used. Understand that in adding two-digit numbers, one adds tens and tens, ones and ones; and sometimes it is necessary to compose a ten.

Progress to Algebra

Name _____

Add Tens

Essential Question How can you add tens?

HANDS ON
Lesson 8.2

Common Core — Number and Operations in Base Ten—1.NBT.C.4
MATHEMATICAL PRACTICES
MP2, MP7

Listen and Draw

Choose a way to show the problem.
Draw a quick picture to show your work.

| | | | | |

| | | | | | |

Math Talk: Possible answer: 20 has 2 tens and 0 ones. 30 has 3 tens and 0 ones. 0 + 0 = 0, so I know my answer will not have any ones.

Problem Type:
Put Together/Take Apart • Total Unknown

FOR THE TEACHER • Read the following problems. Barb has 20 baseball cards. Ed has 30 baseball cards. How many baseball cards do they have? Kyle has 40 baseball cards. Kim has 50 baseball cards. How many baseball cards do they have?

Math Talk MATHEMATICAL PRACTICES 2

Reasoning Why will there be no ones in your answer when you add 20 + 30?

Chapter 8

four hundred forty-three **443**

© Houghton Mifflin Harcourt Publishing Company

Reteach 8.2 ▲ RtI

Name _____
Lesson 8.2
Reteach

Add Tens

What is 10 + 30?

Use ▭▭▭▭.
Start with 1 ten.
Add 3 more tens.
Draw the tens.

| | | |
1 ten + 3 tens = __4__ tens
10 + 30 = __40__

Use ▭▭▭▭. Draw to show tens.
Write how many tens. Write the sum.

1.
1 ten + 8 tens = __9__ tens
10 + 80 = __90__

2.
4 tens + 3 tens = __7__ tens
40 + 30 = __70__

3.
2 tens + 6 tens = __8__ tens
20 + 60 = __80__

4.
5 tens + 3 tens = __8__ tens
50 + 30 = __80__

Chapter Resources
© Houghton Mifflin Harcourt Publishing Company
8-7
Reteach

Enrich 8.2

Differentiated Instruction

Name _____
Lesson 8.2
Enrich

Treasure Tens

Each 🔔 stands for 10. Draw the missing 🔔.
Write the missing numbers.
Then write a number sentence.

1.
__3__ tens + 1 ten = __4__ tens
__30__ + __10__ = __40__

2.
5 tens + __2__ tens = __7__ tens
__50__ + __20__ = __70__

3.
4 tens + __2__ tens = 6 tens
__40__ + __20__ = __60__

Writing and Reasoning Each 🔔 has 10 🪙. Tom has 10 🔔 and 1 🔔. How many 🪙 does Tom have in all?

Tom has 20 dimes.

Chapter Resources
© Houghton Mifflin Harcourt Publishing Company
8-8
Enrich

Model and Draw

How can you find 30 + 40?

$$30 \quad + \quad 40 \quad = \quad \underline{70}$$

$\underline{7}$ tens

 Share and Show 🖊 **MATH BOARD**

Use ▭. Draw to show tens.
Write the sum. Write how many tens.

1. $20 + 40 = \underline{60}$

$\underline{6}$ tens

2. $30 + 30 = \underline{60}$

$\underline{6}$ tens

3. $40 + 50 = \underline{90}$

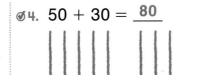

$\underline{9}$ tens

4. $50 + 30 = \underline{80}$

$\underline{8}$ tens

© Houghton Mifflin Harcourt Publishing Company

444 four hundred forty-four

Advanced Learners Kinesthetic Individual / Partners

Materials Coins (see *eTeacher Resources*)

- Have partners use dimes to show tens.
- One child uses the dimes to create a problem. The partner writes the addition sentence to show how many tens there are.
- Partners reverse roles and continue the activity.

3 tens   5 tens

---

③ **EXPLAIN**

Model and Draw Common Core **MATHEMATICAL PRACTICES**

MP4 Model with mathematics. Work through the model together.

- **How can you write 30 + 40 using only tens?** 3 tens + 4 tens
- **What can you draw for a quick picture of 30 + 40?** I can draw 3 lines to show 3 tens and 4 lines to show 4 tens.
- **How can you find the sum of 30 + 40?** Possible answer: I can count all of the tens to find the total of 7 tens, or 70.
- **How can you use your quick picture to help you find the sum of 30 + 40?** I can count the number of lines to find the number of tens.

Share and Show

Have children complete Exercises 1–4 by using base-ten blocks to model the addends and then draw a quick picture to show their work.

- **In Exercise 1, is the sum 6 or 60? Explain.** Possible answer: The sum is 60. There are 6 tens in 60, but 6 on its own means 6 ones.
- **How do you know your answer to Exercise 4 is correct?** Possible answer: I modeled the addends. Each quick picture shows tens. When I count the tens I can see I have 8 tens or 80.

Use the checked exercises for Quick Check.

 Quick Check **RtI**

If a child misses the checked exercises

Then Differentiate Instruction with
- Reteach 8.2
- Personal Math Trainer 1.NBT.C.4
- RtI Tier 1 Activity (online)

⚠ **COMMON ERRORS**

Error Children add the tens but write the sum as ones.

Example In Exercise 3, children write the sum for 40 + 50 as 9.

Springboard to Learning Have children use their quick pictures to explain that each line represents a group of 10. Have children count by tens to find that 9 tens is the same as 90.

Lesson 8.2 444

On Your Own

MP2 Reason abstractly and quantitatively.
If children answered Exercises 3 and 4 correctly, assign Exercises 5–9. Tell children that they may continue to use base-ten blocks if they need to.

Exercise 9 requires children to use higher order thinking skills as they draw a way to add two groups of tens to make 50.

MP7 Look for and make use of structure.
To extend learning, you might pose the following situation.

- **Suppose you need to draw tens you can add to get 30. Are there more ways to add two groups of tens to make a sum of 30 or 50? Explain.** Possible answer: There are more ways to make 50. There are only two ways to add two groups of tens to make 30 but there are four ways to make 50.

MP2 Reason abstractly and quantitatively.

- **Why are there more ways to make 50 than to make 30 by adding tens?** Possible answer: 50 has 5 tens and 30 only has 3 tens. 50 has more tens so there are more ways to combine tens to get 50.

Name _____

On Your Own

MATHEMATICAL PRACTICE 2 **Represent a Problem** Draw to show tens. Write the sum. Write how many tens.

5. $40 + 40 =$ __80__

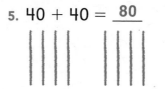

____8____ tens

6. $70 + 20 =$ __90__

____9____ tens

7. $10 + 80 =$ __90__

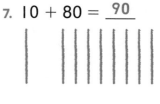

____9____ tens

8. $60 + 30 =$ __90__

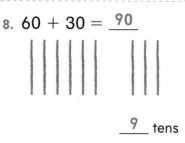

____9____ tens

9. **GO DEEPER** Draw two groups of tens you can add to get a sum of 50. Write the number sentence.

Check that children's drawings match their numbers. Possible answers: $10 + 40 = 50$, $20 + 30 = 50$, $30 + 20 = 50$, $40 + 10 = 50$.

Problem Solving • Applications (Real World)

WRITE) Math

10. *THINK SMARTER* Complete the web. Write the missing addend to get a sum of 90.

Math on the Spot

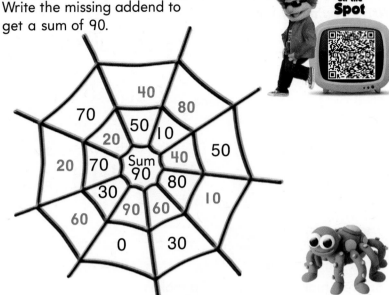

11. *THINK SMARTER* Choose all the ways that name the model.

- ○ 4 ones and 3 tens
- ● 4 tens and 3 tens
- ● 7 tens
- ● 70

 TAKE HOME ACTIVITY • Ask your child to explain how to use tens to find 20 + 70.

446 four hundred forty-six

© Houghton Mifflin Harcourt Publishing Company

DIFFERENTIATED INSTRUCTION   INDEPENDENT ACTIVITIES

Grab-and-Go!

Differentiated Centers Kit

Activities
Groups of Ten

Children complete blue Activity Card 14 by modeling groups of 10.

Literature
It's a Homerun!

Children read the book and add baseball cards.

Problem Solving • Applications (Real World)

THINK SMARTER

MP7 Look for and make use of structure.
Children start at one part of the outer ring and move straight in toward the sum of 90. For each section of the web, they need to find a missing addend. There are a total of 9 missing addends, so encourage children to use a systematic way to be sure they find all the missing addends.

 Math on the Spot Video Tutor
Use this video to help children model and solve this type of *Think Smarter* problem.

 **Math on the Spot** videos are in the Interactive Student Edition and at *www.thinkcentral.com*.

THINK SMARTER

In Exercise 11, children should be able to interpret the quick drawing as a set of 4 tens and a set of 3 tens and recognize that these represent 40, 30, and a sum of 70 (7 tens). Children who select the first choice should identify whether ones or tens are represented in the drawing. Have children use connecting cubes and quick drawings to practice with additional problems if needed.

⑤ EVALUATE Formative Assessment

Essential Question

Reflect Using the Language Objective Have children model and explain to a partner to answer the Essential Question.

How can you add tens? Possible answer: I show tens for both addends. The total number of tens that I have is the sum.

Math Journal  WRITE) Math

Choose an addition problem from the spider web. Draw a quick picture and write the number sentence.

Practice and Homework

Use the Practice and Homework pages to provide children with more practice of the concepts and skills presented in this lesson. Children master their understanding as they complete practice items and then challenge their critical thinking skills with Problem Solving. Use the Write Math section to determine children's understanding of content for this lesson. Encourage children to use their Math Journals to record their answers.

Add Tens

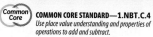
COMMON CORE STANDARD—1.NBT.C.4
Use place value understanding and properties of operations to add and subtract.

Draw to show tens. Write the sum.
Write how many tens.

1. $10 + 30 = \underline{40}$

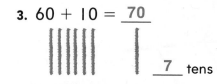

_4_ tens

2. $30 + 30 = \underline{60}$

_6_ tens

3. $60 + 10 = \underline{70}$

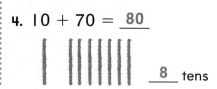

_7_ tens

4. $10 + 70 = \underline{80}$

_8_ tens

Problem Solving · Real World

Draw tens to solve.   Check children's work.

5. Drew makes 20 posters. Tia makes 30 posters. How many posters do they make?

_50_ posters

6. Regina read 40 pages. Alice read 50 pages. How many pages did they read?

_90_ pages

7. **WRITE** Math Choose an addition problem from the spider web on page 446. Draw a quick picture and write the number sentence.

Check children's work.

Chapter 8   four hundred forty-seven **447**

Cross-Curricular   S.T.E.M.

Materials base-ten blocks

- Tell children that some kinds of birds, such as flamingos and penguins, live in big groups. Discuss with children other kinds of animals that they have seen in large groups. Make a list of these animals on the board.
- Have children use base-ten blocks to model different groups of birds. For example, tell children that there are two groups of penguins and 40 penguins in all. Then have children model a way to show 40 as a sum of two numbers using base-ten blocks. For example, children may model 10 + 30. Challenge children to show two other ways.

SOCIAL STUDIES

Materials road map of your state

- Display a map of your state. Use the mileage key to determine a 10-mile increment on the map.
- Start at your city or town and "tour" the area to your north. Travel in multiples of 10 miles. Have children add the two distances. For example:

  Go 20 miles north. What town is nearby?
  Go 50 miles more. How many miles north are we now?
  20 + 50 = 70 miles
  What is in this area?

- Repeat by going south, east, and west of your city or town.

Lesson Check (1.NBT.C.4)

1. What is the sum?
Write the number.

$$20 + 30 = \underline{50}$$

2. What is the sum?
Write the number.

$$30 + 10 = \underline{40}$$

Spiral Review (1.OA.C.6, 1.NBT.B.3)

3. Write a doubles fact that can help you solve $6 + 5 = 11$.

Doubles fact used may vary.

$$\underline{5} + \underline{5} = \underline{10}$$

4. Circle the number sentences that are true.
Cross out the number sentences that are false.

448 four hundred forty-eight

© Houghton Mifflin Harcourt Publishing Company

FOR MORE PRACTICE
GO TO THE
Personal Math Trainer

Hands On • Subtract Tens

LESSON AT A GLANCE

F C R Focus:

Common Core State Standards

1.NBT.C.6 Subtract multiples of 10 in the range 10–90 from multiples of 10 in the range 10–90 (positive or zero differences), using concrete models or drawings and strategies based on place value, properties of operations, and/or the relationship between addition and subtraction; relate the strategy to a written method and explain the reasoning used.

MATHEMATICAL PRACTICES (See *Mathematical Practices in GO Math!* in the *Planning Guide* for full text.) **MP3** Construct viable arguments and critique the reasoning of others. **MP4** Model with mathematics. **MP6** Attend to precision. **MP8** Look for and express regularity in repeated reasoning.

F C R Coherence:

Standards Across the Grades

Before	Grade 1	After
K.NBT.A.1	1.NBT.C.6	2.NBT.B.5

F C R Rigor:

Level 1: Understand Concepts....................*Share and Show* (✓ Checked Items)
Level 2: Procedural Skills and Fluency.......*On Your Own, Practice and Homework*
Level 3: Applications................................*Think Smarter and Go Deeper*

Learning Objective
Draw a model to subtract tens.

Language Objective
Children explain to a partner step-by-step how to subtract tens.

Materials
MathBoard, base-ten blocks, connecting cubes, Workmats 3 and 8 (see *eTeacher Resources*)

F C R For more about how *GO Math!* fosters **Coherence** within the Content Standards and Mathematical Progressions for this chapter, see page 433J.

About the Math

Professional Development

MP1 Make sense of problems and persevere in solving them.

Skilled problem solvers use many approaches to find an answer after they have worked out what the problem means and what question needs to be answered. One approach often used is to create a similar but simpler problem to help determine a way to find the answer.

Given a problem such as 30 − 10, better problem solvers will not count out 30 counters, remove 10 counters, and count to find the difference. Instead, they will first work to make sense of the problem. They may find that if they think of 30 as 3 tens and 10 as 1 ten, they can simply use something they already know (3 − 1 = 2) to help them understand that 30 − 10 can be thought of as 3 tens − 1 ten = 2 tens, or 20.

 Professional Development Videos

 GO DIGITAL

 Interactive Student Edition

Personal Math Trainer

 Math on the Spot Video

 Animated Math Models

iT *iTools:* Base-Ten Blocks

 HMH Mega Math

Daily Routines

Common Core

 Problem of the Day 8.3

Basic Facts Solve. Circle the doubles fact.

$9 + 0 = \underline{9}$ $9 - 9 = \underline{0}$ $9 + 9 = \underline{18}$

Vocabulary

GO DIGITAL
• Interactive Student Edition
• Multimedia eGlossary

Fluency Builder
Subtraction Circle

Common Core Fluency Standard 1.OA.C.6

Materials Math Mountain Cards (see *eTeacher Resources*)

Divide the class into small groups. Have each group form a circle on the floor. Give a volunteer in each group a stack of Math Mountain Cards with facts within 10.

Explain that children should pass the cards around the circle, each child taking one card. When a child receives a card, the child should use the numbers on the card to write a subtraction fact.

10
$10 - 6 = 4$
$10 - 4 = 6$
$-$ $-$
6 $+$ 4

Pages 52–53 in *Strategies and Practice for Skills and Facts Fluency* provide additional fluency support for this lesson.

① ENGAGE

with the Interactive Student Edition

Essential Question
How can you subtract tens?

Making Connections
Ask children to tell what they know about modeling tens.

• **How can you model ten?** I can build a ten-cube train. I can draw a quick picture of ten. I can use one tens-block to show ten.

• **How would you model 30?** Possible answer: 3 tens blocks

• **How would you model 48?** Possible answer: 4 tens blocks and 8 ones blocks

Learning Activity
What problem are children trying to solve? Connect the story to the problem. Ask the following questions.

• **When you model a ten, is it easier to show ten ones or one ten?** 1 ten **Why?** Possible answer: Because it is easier to think of one group of ten than to think of ten individual ones.

• **How is subtracting tens similar to subtracting ones?** Possible answer: To subtract ones or tens, I model the ones or the tens, cross out to show subtraction, and count what is left.

Literacy and Mathematics
Choose from one or more of the following activities.

• Give children a start number, such as 60, and have them count back 3 tens. Repeat with other start numbers.

• As a class, write a story that starts with 90 objects and keeps subtracting ten until zero remain.

② EXPLORE

Listen and Draw

Materials base-ten blocks, connecting cubes, Workmats 3 and 8 (see *eTeacher Resources*)

Some children may use ones to show the problem. Encourage them to trade 10 ones for a ten to find the answer using manipulatives.

Tara has 30 seashells. 20 shells are big. The rest are small. How many small shells does she have? 10 small shells

After modeling the problem, have children draw a picture to show the subtraction.

• **How did you solve the problem?** Possible answer: I put out 3 tens. I moved 2 of them to the side and counted how many were left to find 1 ten, or 10.

• **How does your drawing show the subtraction?** I drew 3 lines for 3 tens. Then I circled 2 of the tens and drew an X through the group of 2 to show what was taken away.

Read the next problem. Have children solve the problem at the bottom of the workspace.

Sammy has 50 shells. He gives 30 shells to his friend. How many shells does Sammy have now? 20 shells

• **How can you solve this problem without models?** I think 5 tens − 3 tens = 2 tens. 2 tens is the same as 20; I can start at 50 and count backwards by tens to subtract 3 tens.

 MP4 Model with mathematics. Use **Math Talk** to focus on children's understanding of subtracting tens.

• **How do the quick pictures help you find the answer?** I can count the tens that aren't crossed out and that tells me how many tens are left.

ELL **Strategy:**
Understand Context

Write **6 − 2 = _____**. Show the problem with base-ten blocks.

Then write **60 − 20 = _____**. Show 6 tens blocks.

• **I start with 6 tens blocks or 60. I take away 20 or 2 tens blocks.** Take away the 2 tens. **I have 4 tens or 40 left. 60 − 40 = 20.**

• **How is subtracting 2 from 6 and 20 from 60 similar? How is it different?** Use the base-ten blocks to show the difference between subtracting tens and subtracting ones.

449 Chapter 8

Progress to Algebra → **1.NBT.C.6** Subtract multiples of 10 in the range 10–90 from multiples of 10 in the range 10–90 (positive or zero differences), using concrete models or drawings and strategies based on place value, properties of operations, and/or the relationship between addition and subtraction; relate the strategy to a written method and explain the reasoning used.

Name _____

Subtract Tens

Essential Question How can you subtract tens?

HANDS ON
Lesson 8.3

 Common Core Number and Operations in Base Ten—1.NBT.C.6
MATHEMATICAL PRACTICES
MP3, MP4, MP6, MP8

Listen and Draw

Choose a way to show the problem. Draw a quick picture to show your work.

Possible drawings shown.

Problem Type:
Put Together/Take Apart •
Addend Unknown

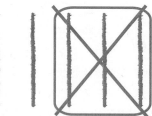

Math Talk: Possible answer: I drew 3 tens to show 30. Then I circled and crossed out 2 tens to show the 20 taken away. I ten is left.

Problem Type:
Take From • Result Unknown

 MATHEMATICAL PRACTICES 4

Represent How does your picture show the first problem?

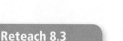 **FOR THE TEACHER •** Read the following problems. Tara has 30 seashells. 20 shells are big. The rest are small. How many small shells does she have? Sammy has 50 shells. He gives 30 shells to his friend. How many shells does Sammy have now?

Chapter 8

four hundred forty-nine **449**

© Houghton Mifflin Harcourt Publishing Company

Reteach 8.3 ▲ RtI

Name _____

Lesson 8.3
Reteach

Subtract Tens

What is 60 − 40?

Use ▭▭. Show 6 tens. Take away 4 tens. 2 tens are left.

6 tens − 4 tens = __2__ tens
60 − 40 = __20__

Use ▭▭. Draw to show tens. Write how many tens. Write the difference.

1.
7 tens − 4 tens = __3__ tens
70 − 40 = __30__

2.
9 tens − 5 tens = __4__ tens
90 − 50 = __40__

3.
5 tens − 2 tens = __3__ tens
50 − 20 = __30__

4.
8 tens − 7 tens = __1__ ten
80 − 70 = __10__

Chapter Resources
© Houghton Mifflin Harcourt Publishing Company
8-9
Reteach

Enrich 8.3 ▶ Differentiated Instruction

Name _____

Lesson 8.3
Enrich

Different Difference

Solve. Cross out the subtraction in each row with the difference that does not match.

1.	80 − 30 = 50	60 − 20 = 40	70 − 20 = 50
2.	70 − 50 = 20	30 − 20 = 10	80 − 70 = 10
3.	90 − 30 = 60	70 − 10 = 60	50 − 20 = 30
4.	60 − 40 = 20	90 − 80 = 10	50 − 40 = 10
5.	40 − 20 = 20	60 − 30 = 30	20 − 0 = 20
6.	90 − 20 = 70	70 − 10 = 60	80 − 10 = 70
7.	80 − 40 = 40	60 − 20 = 40	50 − 20 = 30

Writing and Reasoning How could you change one number in Exercise 1 to make each difference match? Explain.

I could change 60 to 70: 70 − 20 = 50; or

I could change 20 to 10: 60 − 10 = 50.

Chapter Resources
© Houghton Mifflin Harcourt Publishing Company
8-10
Enrich

Model and Draw

How can you find 80 − 30?

$$80 - 30 = \underline{50}$$

_____ 5 _____ tens

 Share and Show MATH BOARD

Use ▭▭▭. Draw to show tens.
Write the difference. Write how many tens.

1. 60 − 20 = __40__

_____ 4 _____ tens

2. 70 − 30 = __40__

_____ 4 _____ tens

3. 80 − 20 = __60__

_____ 6 _____ tens

4. 90 − 40 = __50__

_____ 5 _____ tens

450 four hundred fifty

③ EXPLAIN

Model and Draw (Common Core) MATHEMATICAL PRACTICES

MP4 Model with mathematics. Work through the model and the pictures together.

- **What can you draw to show the subtraction for 80 − 30?** I can draw 8 tens, circle 3 tens, and mark with an X to show 3 tens taken away.

- **How can you find the difference for 80 − 30?** Possible answer: I can start with 8 tens and take away 3 tens. I count how many tens are left. There are 5 tens left, or 50.

- **What other ways can you use to solve 80 − 30?** Possible answers: I can think 8 tens − 3 tens is 5 tens, or 50; I can use tens blocks; I can count back by tens from 80.

Share and Show   MATH BOARD

As children complete Exercises 1–4, have them use base-ten blocks to show the difference, draw quick pictures, and explain their work.

- **In Exercise 1, is the difference 4 or 40? Explain.** The difference is 40. There are 4 tens in 40, but 4 on its own means 4 ones.

- **How do you know your answer is correct?** Possible answer: My drawing shows tens so my answer must be written as tens.

Use the checked exercises for **Quick Check.**

 Quick Check RtI

If ➤ a child misses the checked exercises

Then ➤ Differentiate Instruction with
- Reteach 8.3
- Personal Math Trainer 1.NBT.C.6
- RtI Tier 1 Activity (online)

⚠ COMMON ERRORS

Error Children add instead of subtract.

Example For Exercise 1, children write the difference for 60 − 20 as 80.

Springboard to Learning Have children point to and identify the minus sign. Suggest that they circle the sign as a reminder to subtract. Have children use their quick pictures to check the difference by counting the tens that are not crossed out.

4 ELABORATE

On Your Own

MP6 Attend to precision. If children answered Exercises 3 and 4 correctly, assign Exercises 5–9. Children may continue to use base-ten blocks if they need to.

THINK SMARTER

Exercise 9 requires children to use higher order thinking skills. Have children write the subtraction sentence for the story and the related addition sentence. Children can use a basic fact to identify the number, that when added to 1, will give a sum of 4. Children can then apply this strategy to adding 1 ten and 3 tens for a sum of 4 tens.

Math on the Spot Video Tutor
Use this video to help children model and solve this type of *Think Smarter* problem.

GO DIGITAL Math on the Spot videos are in the Interactive Student Edition and at *www.thinkcentral.com*.

GO DEEPER

Challenge children to discuss different ways they could solve this problem. Make sure that every method results in 30. Other ways to solve might involve properties of operations or different ways to model numbers.

MP3 Construct viable arguments and critique the reasoning of others.

- Compare the strategies used to solve the problem. Which one works the best for you? **Why?** Answers will vary but children's answers should express an understanding of the strategy they selected.

5 EVALUATE Formative Assessment

Essential Question

Reflect Using the Language Objective Have children explain to a partner step-by-step how to answer the Essential Question.

How can you subtract tens? Possible answer: I show tens for the starting number, and then I cross out some tens. The tens that are not crossed out are the difference.

Math Journal  Math

Draw a picture to show how to solve 50 − 40.

Name _____

On Your Own

MATHEMATICAL PRACTICE 6 **Make Connections** Draw to show tens. Write the difference. Write how many tens.

5. $80 - 40 = \underline{40}$

__4__ tens

6. $90 - 70 = \underline{20}$

__2__ tens

7. $70 - 50 = \underline{20}$

__2__ tens

8. $30 - 30 = \underline{0}$

__0__ tens

THINK SMARTER Solve.

9. Jeff has 40 pennies. He gives some to Jill. He has 10 pennies left. How many pennies does Jeff give to Jill?

__30__ pennies

TAKE HOME ACTIVITY • Ask your child to explain how to use tens to find 90 − 70.

Chapter 8 • Lesson 3   four hundred fifty-one **451**

DIFFERENTIATED INSTRUCTION **INDEPENDENT ACTIVITIES**

Differentiated Centers Kit

Activities
Groups of Ten

Children complete blue Activity Card 14 by modeling groups of 10.

Literature
It's a Homerun!

Children read the book and add baseball cards.

Name _____

 Mid-Chapter Checkpoint

 **Personal Math Trainer** Online Assessment and Intervention

Concepts and Skills

Add or subtract. (1.0A.C.6)

| 1. $\begin{array}{r} 4 \\ +8 \\ \hline 12 \end{array}$ | 2. $\begin{array}{r} 15 \\ -7 \\ \hline 8 \end{array}$ | 3. $\begin{array}{r} 9 \\ -6 \\ \hline 3 \end{array}$ | 4. $\begin{array}{r} 3 \\ +1 \\ \hline 4 \end{array}$ | 5. $\begin{array}{r} 10 \\ +6 \\ \hline 16 \end{array}$ | 6. $\begin{array}{r} 11 \\ -2 \\ \hline 9 \end{array}$ |

Use . Draw to show tens.
Write the sum. Write how many tens. (1.NBT.C.4)

7. $30 + 50 = \underline{80}$

||| ||||| _8_ tens

8. $40 + 20 = \underline{60}$

|||| _6_ tens

Use . Draw to show tens.
Write the difference. Write how many tens. (1.NBT.C.6)

9. $90 - 20 = \underline{70}$

_7_ tens

10. $60 - 40 = \underline{20}$

_2_ tens

11. **THINK SMARTER** Mike has 60 marbles. He gives 20 to Kathy. How many marbles does Mike have left? Show your work. (1.NBT.C.6)

_40_ marbles

Check children's work.

© Houghton Mifflin Harcourt Publishing Company

452 four hundred fifty-two

Formative Assessment

Use the **Mid-Chapter Checkpoint** to assess children's learning and progress in the first half of the chapter. The formative assessment provides the opportunity to adjust teaching methods for individual or whole class instruction.

THINK SMARTER

Exercise 11 assesses whether children can subtract tens. Children who answer incorrectly may add instead of subtract. Another common error is to write 4 tens as 4 rather than 40. Use place-value manipulatives, quick drawings, or a hundreds chart to reinforce the similarities between 4, 4 tens, and 40.

✓ Data-Driven Decision Making ▲ RtI

Based on the results of the Mid-Chapter Checkpoint, use the following resources to strengthen individual or whole class instruction.

Item	Lesson	Standards	Common Error	Personal Math Trainer	Intervene With
1–6	8.1	1.OA.C.6	May confuse operation symbols	1.OA.C.6	R—8.1
7, 8	8.2	1.NBT.C.4	May incorrectly model tens	1.NBT.C.4	R—8.2
9–11	8.3	1.NBT.C.6	May add instead of subtract	1.NBT.C.6	R—8.3

Key: R—Reteach (in the *Chapter Resources*)

Practice and Homework

Use the Practice and Homework pages to provide children with more practice of the concepts and skills presented in this lesson. Children master their understanding as they complete practice items and then challenge their critical thinking skills with Problem Solving. Use the Write Math section to determine children's understanding of content for this lesson. Encourage children to use their Math Journals to record their answers.

Name _____

Subtract Tens

Draw to show tens. Write the difference. Write how many tens.

 COMMON CORE STANDARD—1.NBT.C.6
Use place value understanding and properties of operations to add and subtract.

1. 40 − 10 = __30__

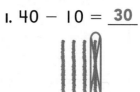

__3__ tens

2. 80 − 40 = __40__

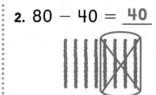

__4__ tens

Problem Solving

Draw tens to solve.

Check children's drawings.

3. Mario has 70 baseball cards. He gives 30 to Lisa. How many baseball cards does Mario have left?

__40__ baseball cards

4. **WRITE** Math Draw a picture to show how to solve 50 − 40.

Check children's work.

© Houghton Mifflin Harcourt Publishing Company

Chapter 8

four hundred fifty-three **453**

Lesson Check (1.NBT.C.6)

1. What is the difference?
Write the number.

$$60 - 20 = \underline{40}$$

2. What is the difference?
Write the number.

$$70 - 30 = \underline{40}$$

Spiral Review (1.OA.C.6, 1.NBT.B.3)

3. Use ○ ● and a ten frame. Show
both addends. Draw to make ten.
Then write a new fact. Add.

9
+ 4

 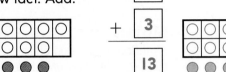

4. Bo crosses out the number cards that are
less than 33 or greater than 38.
What number cards are left?

Number cards __36__ and __37__ are left.

FOR MORE PRACTICE
GO TO THE
Personal Math Trainer

Continue concepts and skills practice with Lesson Check. Use Spiral Review to engage children in previously taught concepts and to promote content retention. Common Core standards are correlated to each section.

Monitoring Common Core Success

Maintaining Focus on the Major Work

Part of the major work in Grade 1 is to solve problems involving addition and subtraction (1.OA.A). In Lesson 8.1, children add and subtract within 20 using a strategy they have already learned. In Lesson 8.2, children add a two-digit number to a multiple of ten (1.NBT.C.4). Then they learn to subtract multiples of 10 from multiples of 10 using base-ten blocks for modeling (1.NBT.C.6). Through the use of basic facts, mathematics modeling, and problem solving tools, children become more prepared to solve advanced addition problems.

Connecting Content Across Domains and Clusters

In Lesson 8.1, a connection is made between Cluster 1.OA.C and Cluster 1.NBT.C, children use strategies such as doubles minus one, related facts, and drawings to add and subtract within 20. They will connect Cluster 1.OA.C to Cluster 1.NBT.C in Lessons 8.2 and 8.3 when children use base ten models and quick pictures to add and subtract tens. Both of these clusters can be directly connected to Cluster 1.OA.A. Children use the skills attained in Lessons 8.1–8.3 to solve addition and subtraction word problems.

Building Fluency

In Lesson 8.1, children add and subtract within 20 (1.OA.C.6). Addition and subtraction skills continue to expand while children work to add and subtract tens. Fluency in addition and subtraction and the process of using appropriate problem solving strategies is further advanced in Lessons 8.2–8.3. Children use applicable mathematics tools, quantitative reasoning, mathematical modeling, and abstract thinking to become fluent in adding and subtracting within 10.

Build fluency with associated fact fluency activities and strengthen children's proficiency with various math strategies. Use *Strategies and Practices for Skills and Fact Fluency —Primary, GK–3*: Level 2, Worksheets 12A–12B to strengthen children's mastery of adding and subtracting within 10.

Use a Hundred Chart to Add

LESSON AT A GLANCE

FOCUS **COHERENCE** **RIGOR**

F C R Focus:

Common Core State Standards

1.NBT.C.4 Add within 100, including adding a two-digit number and a one-digit number, and adding a two-digit number and a multiple of 10, using concrete models or drawings and strategies based on place value, properties of operations, and/or the relationship between addition and subtraction; relate the strategy to a written method and explain the reasoning used. Understand that in adding two-digit numbers, one adds tens and tens, ones and ones; and sometimes it is necessary to compose a ten.

MATHEMATICAL PRACTICES (See *Mathematical Practices in GO Math!* in the *Planning Guide* for full text.)
MP4 Model with mathematics. **MP5** Use appropriate tools strategically. **MP6** Attend to precision.

F C R Coherence:

Standards Across the Grades
Before	Grade 1	After
K.NBT.A.1	1.NBT.C.4	2.NBT.B.5

F C R Rigor:

Level 1: Understand Concepts....................*Share and Show* (✓ Checked Items)
Level 2: Procedural Skills and Fluency.......*On Your Own, Practice and Homework*
Level 3: Applications................................*Think Smarter and Go Deeper*

Learning Objective
Use a hundred chart to find sums.

Language Objective
Children select a number and then demonstrate to a partner how to use a hundred chart to count on by ones or tens.

Materials
MathBoard, Hundred Chart
(see *eTeacher Resources*)

F C R For more about how *GO Math!* fosters **Coherence** within the Content Standards and Mathematical Progressions for this chapter, see page 433J.

About the Math
Professional Development

Progress to Algebra
Why Teach This

A hundred chart is another tool that can be used to show children "why addition works." Children are familiar with a counting on strategy for basic facts. Hundred charts allow children to visually follow along and see how the numbers grow as they apply the counting on strategy to greater numbers. They can touch each number as they count on across the row to add ones, or count on down the columns to add tens.

Exposure to different methods that are efficient and useful with many numbers can help children build their mental math skills.

 Professional Development Videos

 GO DIGITAL

 **SE Interactive Student Edition**

Personal Math Trainer

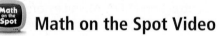 **Math on the Spot Video**

*i*T *i*Tools: Number Charts

Daily Routines

Common Core

 Problem of the Day 8.4

Number of the Day

I am just before 9.   Double me to get 16.
I am just after 7.
What number am I? 8

Have children make up their own riddles
with an answer of 8.

Vocabulary

GO DIGITAL
• Interactive Student Edition
• Multimedia eGlossary

Vocabulary Builder
Tens and Ones
Puzzlers

| ten | | ones |

Materials Vocabulary Cards ten, ones
(see *eTeacher Resources*)

Display and read the Vocabulary Cards.
Then write a two-digit number on the
board. Discuss which digit shows the
number of ones and which shows the
number of tens. Challenge children to write
other two-digit numbers following these
directions.

• **Write a two-digit number with 0 ones.**

• **Write a two-digit number with the same
  number of ones and tens.**

• **Write a two-digit number with 6 tens.**

• **Write a two-digit number with 6 ones.**

• **Did everyone write the same number?
  Why or why not?**

Discuss children's responses.

① ENGAGE

with the Interactive Student Edition

Essential Question

How can you use a hundred chart to count on by ones or tens?

Making Connections

Ask children to tell what they know about counting on.

• **When do you use the "counting on" strategy?** Possible answer:
  When I want to add a small number, like 1, 2, or 3.

• **What number do you start with when you count on by ones?** The
  larger number.

Learning Activity

What problem are children trying to solve? Connect the story to the
problem. Ask the following questions.

• **When you add 10, do you count on by ten ones or one ten?** One
  ten **Why?** Because one ten is one group of ten ones so you count on by
  one group

• **How do you count on by ones and tens if you add 34 to a
  number?** You count on 3 tens and 4 ones

Literacy and Mathematics

Choose from one or more of the following activities.

• Have children make up addition stories and have others say if they
  add ones, tens, or both.

• Have children act out two-digit numbers by hopping forward
  for each ten and stepping to the right for each one as they say
  the number their movement represents. So for 12, children hop
  forward one time as they say 10 and then step right 2 times as
  they say 11, 12.

EXPLORE

Listen and Draw

Materials Hundred Chart (see eTeacher Resources)
Read the following problem aloud.

Alice picks 12 flowers. Then she picks 4 more flowers. How many flowers does Alice pick?

Tell children they can use the hundred chart on their page to solve the problem. Children may prefer to use the Hundred Chart instead.

- **Start at 12. Count on 4 spaces to the right. Where do you stop?** 16 **How does using a hundred chart help you count on by ones?** Possible answer: As I move to the right across the row, each space shows the number that is one more.

Now read the next problem aloud.

Ella picks 10 strawberries. Then she picks 20 more strawberries. How many strawberries does Ella pick?

- **Start at 10. Move down the column 2 rows, or 2 tens. Where do you stop?** 30 **How can the hundred chart help you count on by tens?** Possible answer: As I move down the column, each space shows the number that is ten more.

As time allows, present different problems for children to solve using the hundred chart.

 MP6 Attend to precision.
Use **Math Talk** to focus on children's understanding of how to use a hundred chart to add ones and tens.

- **How many do you add to your current number if you move down a row in a hundred chart? Why?** Possible answer: 10. There are 10 squares in each row.

ELL **Strategy:**
Model Concepts

Direct children's attention to the hundred chart.

Review the ten more patterns on the chart by reminding children that the number below any number is ten more than the number.

- **What is ten more than 20?** 30

Write the problem 16 + 20 = _____.

- **Find 16. What is ten more than 16?** 26 **What is 20 more than 16?** 36. **16 + 20 = 36.**

Pose some other addition problems for children to solve using the hundred chart.

1.NBT.C.4 Add within 100, including adding a two-digit number and a one-digit number, and adding a two-digit number and a multiple of 10, using concrete models or drawings and strategies based on place value, properties of operations, and/or the relationship between addition and subtraction; relate the strategy to a written method and explain the reasoning used. Understand that in adding two-digit numbers, one adds tens and tens, ones and ones; and sometimes it is necessary to compose a ten.

Progress to Algebra

Name _____

Lesson 8.4

Use a Hundred Chart to Add

Essential Question How can you use a hundred chart to count on by ones or tens?

Common Core **Number and Operations in Base Ten—1.NBT.C.4**
MATHEMATICAL PRACTICES
MP4, MP5, MP6

Listen and Draw

Use the hundred chart to solve the problems.

1	2	3	4	5	6	7	8	9	10
11	12	13	14	15	16	17	18	19	20
21	22	23	24	25	26	27	28	29	30
31	32	33	34	35	36	37	38	39	40
41	42	43	44	45	46	47	48	49	50
51	52	53	54	55	56	57	58	59	60
61	62	63	64	65	66	67	68	69	70
71	72	73	74	75	76	77	78	79	80
81	82	83	84	85	86	87	88	89	90
91	92	93	94	95	96	97	98	99	100

Possible answer: To find how many flowers Alice picks, I put my finger on 12, then count on 4 ones to the right. I end on 16, so Alice picks 16 flowers. To find how many strawberries Ella picks, I put my finger on 10, then move down 2 rows to count on 2 tens. I end on 30, so Ella picks 30 strawberries.

FOR THE TEACHER • Read the following problems.
Alice picks 12 flowers. Then she picks 4 more flowers. How many flowers does Alice pick? Ella picks 10 strawberries. Then she picks 20 more strawberries. How many strawberries does Ella pick?

Chapter 8 **Problem Type:**
Add To • Result Unknown

 MATHEMATICAL PRACTICES 6

Explain how you can use a hundred chart to find each sum.

four hundred fifty-five **455**

Reteach 8.4 RtI

Name _____

Lesson 8.4 Reteach

Use a Hundred Chart to Add

You can count on to add on a hundred chart.

Start at 21. Move right to count on 3 ones. Count
22 , 23 , 24
21 + 3 = 24

Start at 68. Move down to count on 3 tens. Count
78 , 88 , 98
68 + 30 = 98

Use the hundred chart to add.
Count on by ones.

1. 46 + 2 = 48   2. 63 + 3 = 66

Count on by tens.

3. 52 + 30 = 82   4. 23 + 40 = 63

Chapter Resources
© Houghton Mifflin Harcourt Publishing Company
8-11
Reteach

Enrich 8.4 **Differentiated Instruction**

Name _____

Lesson 8.4 Enrich

Add Some Color

1	2	3	4	5	6	7	8	9	10
11	12	13	14	15	16	17	18	19	20
21	22	23	24	25	26	27	28	29	30
31	32	33	34	35	36	37	38	39	40
41	42	43	44	45	46	47	48	49	50
51	52	53	54	55	56	57	58	59	60
61	62	63	64	65	66	67	68	69	70
71	72	73	74	75	76	77	78	79	80
81	82	83	84	85	86	87	88	89	90
91	92	93	94	95	96	97	98	99	100

Use the hundred chart to add. Color the sum.

1. 40 + 17 = 57   2. 24 + 40 = 64
3. 72 + 3 = 75   4. 42 + 4 = 46
5. 20 + 33 = 53   6. 33 + 2 = 35
7. 5 + 61 = 66   8. 14 + 30 = 44

Writing and Reasoning Explain two ways to use the hundred chart to find a sum of 95.

Possible answer: Start at 91 and count on
4 ones. Start at 25 and count on 7 tens.

Chapter Resources
© Houghton Mifflin Harcourt Publishing Company
8-12
Enrich

Model and Draw

Count on a hundred chart to find a sum.

Start at **24**.
Count on four ones.
25, 26, 27, 28

$24 + 4 = \underline{28}$

1	2	3	4	5	6	7	8	9	10
11	12	13	14	15	16	17	18	19	20
21	22	23	24	25	26	27	28	29	30
31	32	33	34	35	36	37	38	39	40
41	42	43	44	45	46	47	48	49	50
51	52	53	54	55	56	57	58	59	60
61	62	63	64	65	66	67	68	69	70
71	72	73	74	75	76	77	78	79	80
81	82	83	84	85	86	87	88	89	90
91	92	93	94	95	96	97	98	99	100

Start at **31**.
Count on four tens.
41, 51, 61, 71

$31 + 40 = \underline{71}$

Share and Show MATH BOARD

Use the hundred chart to add. Count on by ones or tens.

1. $42 + 7 = \underline{49}$

2. $57 + 30 = \underline{87}$

3. $91 + 5 = \underline{96}$

4. $18 + 50 = \underline{68}$

© Houghton Mifflin Harcourt Publishing Company

Advanced Learners

 Visual / Kinesthetic Partners

Materials Hundred Chart (see *eTeacher Resources*), crayons

- Present the following to children: **Karen has 32 stickers. She buys a sheet of 20 stickers. Then her mom gives her 5 stickers. How many stickers does Karen have now?**

- Have partners use the Hundred Chart, coloring to show how they solved. Then have them write the addition sentence.

- **How did you find the answer?**
  Possible answer: I started at 32 and counted on 2 tens to get to 52. Then I counted on 5 ones to get to 57.

- **What is the addition sentence?**
  $32 + 20 + 5 = 57$

1	2	3	4	5	6	7	8	9	10
11	12	13	14	15	16	17	18	19	20
21	22	23	24	25	26	27	28	29	30
31	32	33	34	35	36	37	38	39	40
41	42	43	44	45	46	47	48	49	50
51	52	53	54	55	56	57	58	59	60

- Have partners create and exchange similar addition stories to solve on the Hundred Chart.

---

③ EXPLAIN

Model and Draw  MATHEMATICAL PRACTICES

MP4 Model with mathematics. Work through the model with children. Have children trace to write the sum 28.

- **If you move across from 24 to 28 on the hundred chart, how many have you added to 24?** 4 ones, or 4

Work through the model with children. Have children trace to write the sum 71.

- **If you move down from 31 to 71 on the hundred chart, how many have you added to 31?** 4 tens, or 40

Share and Show   MATH BOARD

Have children use the hundred chart to complete Exercises 1–4. Read each exercise and have children tell whether they will count on by ones or tens.

- **How could you use the hundred chart to add 60 to 29?** Start at 29. Move down 6 rows to 89.

- **How do you know your answer is correct?** I use the hundred chart to count on by ones or tens.

Use the checked exercises for **Quick Check**.

 ### Quick Check  **RtI**

If ▶ a child misses the checked exercises

Then ▶ **Differentiate Instruction** with
- Reteach 8.4
- Personal Math Trainer 1.NBT.C.4
- RtI Tier 1 Activity (online)

⚠ COMMON ERRORS

Error Children may always count on by ones.

Example In Exercise 2, children write a sum of 60.

Springboard to Learning Have children decide if they are adding ones or tens. Remind them that when they add ones, they count across on the hundred chart. When they add tens, they count down on the hundred chart.

Lesson 8.4 456

4 ELABORATE

On Your Own

MP5 Use appropriate tools strategically. If children answered Exercises 3 and 4 correctly, assign Exercises 5–11. Work through the model with children to find each sum, reinforcing the use of a hundred chart to find sums.

Point out that Exercise 11 is different from the other exercises. Remind children that when they add three numbers they add two numbers and then add the other number to the sum of the first two numbers.

GO DEEPER

MP6 Attend to precision. Exercise 11 requires children to use higher order thinking skills as they use the hundred chart to add 3 numbers. Have children use the hundred chart to solve the problem. Have them use the Commutative Property of Addition by starting with a different addend to solve the problem. Be sure children remember to add all three numbers.

GO DEEPER

MP2 Reason abstractly and quantitatively. To extend thinking, challenge children to solve the following addition problems. Children will utilize their critical thinking and reasoning skills as they determine that they must move to the next row when adding ones, or move in two ways on the hundred chart to add both tens and ones. Have volunteers share their solutions.

$55 + 6 =$ ___61___

$13 + 9 =$ ___22___

$36 + 51 =$ ___87___

$81 + 18 =$ ___99___

MP6 Attend to precision.

- **How can you use the hundred chart to add 36 to 51?** Possible answer: I can start on 51, count down 3 rows to add 30, then move to the right 6 spaces to add the 6 ones.

- **Why did you have to move in two directions on the hundred chart?** Possible answer: 36 has both tens and ones so I need to move down to add the tens and move to the right to add the ones.

Name _____

On Your Own

1	2	3	4	5	6	7	8	9	10
11	12	13	14	15	16	17	18	19	20
21	22	23	24	25	26	27	28	29	30
31	32	33	34	35	36	37	38	39	40
41	42	43	44	45	46	47	48	49	50
51	52	53	54	55	56	57	58	59	60
61	62	63	64	65	66	67	68	69	70
71	72	73	74	75	76	77	78	79	80
81	82	83	84	85	86	87	88	89	90
91	92	93	94	95	96	97	98	99	100

How can you use the hundred chart to find each sum?

$32 + 5 =$ ___37___

$48 + 30 =$ ___78___

MATHEMATICAL PRACTICE 5 **Use Appropriate Tools**
Use the hundred chart to add.
Count on by ones or tens.

5. $13 + 70 =$ ___83___   6. $22 + 6 =$ ___28___

7. $71 + 3 =$ ___74___   8. $49 + 50 =$ ___99___

9. $53 + 4 =$ ___57___   10. $25 + 40 =$ ___65___

11. **GO DEEPER** Solve. Show your work. Check children's work.

$31 + 20 + 40 =$ ___91___

© Houghton Mifflin Harcourt Publishing Company

Chapter 8 • Lesson 4   four hundred fifty-seven **457**

Problem Solving • Applications 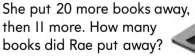 WRITE Math

Choose a way to solve. Draw or
write to show your work.

12. THINK SMARTER Rae put 20 books away.
She put 20 more books away,
then 11 more. How many
books did Rae put away?

51 books

Personal Math Trainer

13. THINK SMARTER+ Use
the hundred chart
to add. Count on
by ones or tens.

1	2	3	4	5	6	7	8	9	10
11	12	13	14	15	16	17	18	19	20
21	22	23	24	25	26	27	28	29	30
31	32	33	34	35	36	37	38	39	40
41	42	43	44	45	46	47	48	49	50
51	52	53	54	55	56	57	58	59	60
61	62	63	64	65	66	67	68	69	70
71	72	73	74	75	76	77	78	79	80
81	82	83	84	85	86	87	88	89	90
91	92	93	94	95	96	97	98	99	100

$62 + 9 =$ **71**

Explain how you used the chart to find the sum.

Possible answer: I start at 62. I count on 9 ones.

 TAKE HOME ACTIVITY • On a piece of paper, write 36 + 40.
Ask your child to explain how to use the hundred chart to
count on by tens to find the sum.

458 four hundred fifty-eight

DIFFERENTIATED INSTRUCTION — INDEPENDENT ACTIVITIES

Differentiated Centers Kit

Activities
Count On

Children complete
blue Activity Card
20 by counting on
to add two-digit
numbers.

Literature
It's a Homerun!

Children read the
book and add
baseball cards.

Problem Solving • Applications

MP6 Attend to precision. Have children
solve each problem. Children may need to use
a hundred chart.

THINK SMARTER

**MP2 Reason abstractly and
quantitatively.** In Exercise 12 children solve
a two-step problem. Have children explain
which strategies they used to solve this
problem.

 ### Math on the Spot
Video Tutor
Use this video to help children model and solve
this type of *Think Smarter* problem.

 Math on the Spot videos are in the Interactive
Student Edition and at *www.thinkcentral.com*.

THINK SMARTER+
Personal Math Trainer
Be sure to assign Exercise 13 to children in the
Personal Math Trainer. It features a video to
help them model and answer the problem.
This item assesses whether children know how
to use a hundred chart to count on by ones
or tens. Children who answer incorrectly may
count on by tens, moving down the chart,
instead of ones, moving across the chart.

⑤ EVALUATE Formative Assessment

Essential Question

Reflect Using the Language Objective Have
children select a number then demonstrate to
a partner to answer the Essential Question.

**How can you use a hundred chart to count
on by ones or tens?** Possible answer: I start at the
number and then move one space to the right for each
one I add. I start at the number and then move down one
row for each ten I add.

Math Journal WRITE Math

**Write a number sentence to add 6 ones
to 21. Write a number sentence to add
6 tens to 21.**

Practice and Homework

Use the Practice and Homework pages to provide children with more practice of the concepts and skills presented in this lesson. Children master their understanding as they complete practice items and then challenge their critical thinking skills with Problem Solving. Use the Write Math section to determine children's understanding of content for this lesson. Encourage children to use their Math Journals to record their answers.

Use a Hundred Chart to Add

COMMON CORE STANDARD—1.NBT.C.4
Use place value understanding and properties of operations to add and subtract.

Use the hundred chart to add.
Count on by ones or tens.

1. $47 + 2 = $ ___49___

2. $26 + 50 = $ ___76___

3. $22 + 5 = $ ___27___

4. $4 + 85 = $ ___89___

1	2	3	4	5	6	7	8	9	10
11	12	13	14	15	16	17	18	19	20
21	22	23	24	25	26	27	28	29	30
31	32	33	34	35	36	37	38	39	40
41	42	43	44	45	46	47	48	49	50
51	52	53	54	55	56	57	58	59	60
61	62	63	64	65	66	67	68	69	70
71	72	73	74	75	76	77	78	79	80
81	82	83	84	85	86	87	88	89	90
91	92	93	94	95	96	97	98	99	100

Problem Solving (Real World)

Choose a way to solve. Draw or write to show your work.

5. 17 children are on the bus. Then 20 more children get on the bus. How many children are on the bus now?

   Check children's work.
   $17 + 20 = 37$
   ___37___ children

6. **WRITE Math** Write a number sentence to add 6 ones to 21. Write a number sentence to add 6 tens to 21.

   Check children's work.
   _____
   _____
   _____

© Houghton Mifflin Harcourt Publishing Company

Common Core PROFESSIONAL DEVELOPMENT — Math Talk in Action

After completing Exercises 1–4, discuss approaches children used for Exercise 4.

Teacher: How is Exercise 4 different from Exercise 3?

Kate: The first number is smaller than the second number.

Sam: It took longer to do.

Teacher: What do you mean, Sam?

Sam: I had to count on 8 tens and then count on 5 ones. It took me a long time to do that.

Teacher: Did anyone use a different way to find the answer?

Babs: I changed the order of the addends so I could add 4 to 85.

Zoe: I thought of 85 as 8 tens plus 5 ones. I changed the problem to 8 tens plus 5 ones plus 4 ones.

Sam: I guess I should think about a problem before I start working on it. Both of those ways are shorter than what I did.

Teacher: That is an important point, Sam. Thinking about a problem and what it means before you solve it is a smart thing to do.

Ben: There sure are a lot of ways to do that problem!

Teacher: Yes. Remember you should always use a way that makes sense to you.

1. What is the sum?
   Write the number.

   $42 + 50 =$ __92__

1	2	3	4	5	6	7	8	9	10
11	12	13	14	15	16	17	18	19	20
21	22	23	24	25	26	27	28	29	30
31	32	33	34	35	36	37	38	39	40
41	42	43	44	45	46	47	48	49	50
51	52	53	54	55	56	57	58	59	60
61	62	63	64	65	66	67	68	69	70
71	72	73	74	75	76	77	78	79	80
81	82	83	84	85	86	87	88	89	90
91	92	93	94	95	96	97	98	99	100

2. What is the sum?
   Write the number.

   $11 + 8 =$ __19__

3. Use mental math.
   What number is ten less than 52?
   Write the number.

   __42__

4. Write an addition fact that helps
   you solve $16 - 9$.

   __9__ + __7__ = __16__

FOR MORE PRACTICE
GO TO THE
Personal Math Trainer

© Houghton Mifflin Harcourt Publishing Company

460 four hundred sixty

Continue concepts and skills practice with
Lesson Check. Use Spiral Review to engage
children in previously taught concepts and to
promote content retention. Common Core
standards are correlated to each section.

Hands On • Use Models to Add

LESSON AT A GLANCE

F C R Focus:

Common Core State Standards

■ **1.NBT.C.4** Add within 100, including adding a two-digit number and a one-digit number, and adding a two-digit number and a multiple of 10, using concrete models or drawings and strategies based on place value, properties of operations, and/or the relationship between addition and subtraction; relate the strategy to a written method and explain the reasoning used. Understand that in adding two-digit numbers, one adds tens and tens, ones and ones; and sometimes it is necessary to compose a ten.

MATHEMATICAL PRACTICES (See *Mathematical Practices in GO Math!* in the *Planning Guide* for full text.)
MP4 Model with mathematics. **MP6** Attend to precision.

F C R Coherence:

Standards Across the Grades
Before　　**Grade 1**　**After**
K.NBT.A.1　1.NBT.C.4　2.NBT.B.5

F C R Rigor:

Level 1: Understand Concepts.....................*Share and Show* (✓ Checked Items)
Level 2: Procedural Skills and Fluency.......*On Your Own, Practice and Homework*
Level 3: Applications...............................*Think Smarter and Go Deeper*

Learning Objective
Use concrete models to add ones or tens to a two-digit number.

Language Objective
Children first listen to a partner explain, and then rephrase in their own words how models can help you add ones or tens to a two-digit number.

Materials
MathBoard, base-ten blocks

F C R For more about how *GO Math!* fosters **Coherence** within the Content Standards and Mathematical Progressions for this chapter, see page 433J.

About the Math
Professional Development

Progress to Algebra
Using Quick Pictures

Quick pictures provide an easy way to model because the drawings can be made quickly and simply. When you first introduce quick pictures, explain that these drawings will be used to record the work children have done with base-ten blocks. Point out that it is important to make accurate drawings of the number of tens and the number of ones used, but that it is not important that the drawings look exactly like the base-ten blocks. Have children practice drawing lines and dots to represent tens and ones until they can do this easily and efficiently.

Tell children that they will use their quick pictures to help them visualize addition and subtraction problems. As they build their number and operation concepts, they may stop using the base-ten blocks to model the problems and use quick pictures as a pictorial model instead. They may also use quick pictures as a way to check computations.

 Professional Development Videos

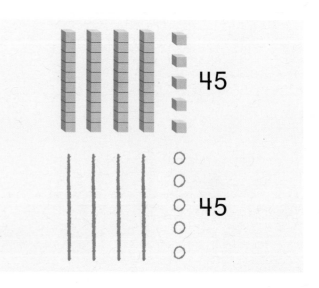

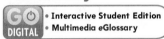
① ENGAGE

with the Interactive Student Edition

Essential Question
How can models help you add ones or tens to a two-digit number?

Making Connections
Ask children to tell what they know about place value and two-digit numbers.

- **What is a two-digit number?** A number that has both ones and tens.

- **What is another way to say 36?** 3 tens and 6 ones

Learning Activity
What problem are children trying to solve? Connect the story to the problem. Ask the following questions.

- **Why do you use different blocks to model tens and ones?** Possible answer: A tens block represents 10 ones or one group of ten; a ones block represents one one.

- **How do the models help you add two-digit numbers?** I can count the ones and the tens to find out how many in all.

Literacy and Mathematics
Choose from one or more of the following activities.

- Have partners make up a poem or song about adding to a two-digit number.

- Have children write a "How To" paragraph about adding two-digit numbers with models.

2 EXPLORE

Progress to Algebra

1.NBT.C.4 Add within 100, including adding a two-digit number and a one-digit number, and adding a two-digit number and a multiple of 10, using concrete models or drawings and strategies based on place value, properties of operations, and/or the relationship between addition and subtraction; relate the strategy to a written method and explain the reasoning used. Understand that in adding two-digit numbers, one adds tens and tens, ones and ones; and sometimes it is necessary to compose a ten.

Listen and Draw

Materials base-ten blocks

Remind children that they used a hundred chart to add ones or tens to a two-digit number. Explain that they will use and draw base-ten blocks to add tens or ones to two-digit numbers. Read the following problem aloud.

Amir counts 14 cars as they go by. Then he counts 5 more cars. How many cars does Amir count?

Have children locate the addition sentence.

• **How do the numbers in the problem match the addition sentence?** Possible answer: The numbers in the problem are the addends. I know 14 is how many cars Amir counts first and 5 is how many more cars he counts.

• **What can you draw to show the addends?** Possible answer: I can draw a line to show 1 ten and 4 circles to show 4 ones. Then I can draw 5 more circles to show 5 ones.

• **What do you write to solve the addition sentence?** I write the sum. The sum is 19.

 Math Talk **MP4 Model with mathematics.** Use **Math Talk** to focus on children's understanding of adding ones or tens to a two-digit number.

• **How does your drawing help you find the answer?** I draw 5 circles to show the 5 cars, then I label the circles to show how I count on to find the answer.

ELL Strategy:
Understand Context

Use base-ten blocks to build understanding in context.

Write **23 + 4 = _____**. Show the problem with base-ten blocks. Explain how to find the sum.

• **I can start with 23 and count on four or I can add the ones cubes together. 3 + 4 = 7. I have 2 tens or 20 and 7 ones. 23 + 4 = 27.**

Point out that the ones blocks are counted together.

MP6 Attend to precision. Why is it important to be precise when you draw your model. The model shows the pieces of the story. If I draw the wrong pieces my answer will not be correct.

Name _____

Use Models to Add

Essential Question How can models help you add ones or tens to a two-digit number?

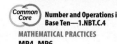 **Common Core** **Number and Operations in Base Ten—1.NBT.C.4**
MATHEMATICAL PRACTICES
MP4, MP6

Listen and Draw

Draw to show how you can find the sum.

Possible answer shown.

 (base-ten drawing with circles labeled 14, 15, 16, 17, 18, 19)

$14 + 5 = \underline{19}$

Math Talk: Possible answer: I drew a picture to represent the 14 cars Amir counted first. Then I drew to show 5 more cars. I started at 14 and counted on to find the total number of cars: 14, 15, 16, 17, 18, 19.

Problem Type:
Add To • Result Unknown

 FOR THE TEACHER • Read the following problem. Amir counts 14 cars as they go by. Then he counts 5 more cars. How many cars does Amir count?

Math Talk MATHEMATICAL PRACTICES 4
Model Explain how you found the sum.

Chapter 8

four hundred sixty-one **461**

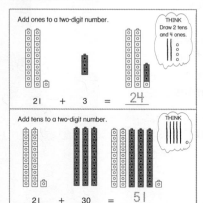

Reteach 8.5 ▲ RtI

Name _____

Lesson 8.5
Reteach

Use Models to Add

Add ones to a two-digit number.
THINK Draw 2 tens and 4 ones.

21 + 3 = __24__

Add tens to a two-digit number.
THINK

21 + 30 = __51__

Use. Draw to show how to add the ones or tens. Write the sum.
Check children's drawings.

1. 15 + 2 = __17__   2. 15 + 20 = __35__

Chapter Resources   8-13   Reteach
© Houghton Mifflin Harcourt Publishing Company

Enrich 8.5 **Differentiated Instruction**

Name _____

Lesson 8.5
Enrich

Tens or Ones?
Circle the correct addend.

1. $52 + \begin{array}{c} 3 \\ \circled{30} \end{array} = 82$ 2. $12 + \begin{array}{c} \circled{7} \\ 70 \end{array} = 19$

3. $44 + \begin{array}{c} \circled{4} \\ 40 \end{array} = 48$ 4. $33 + \begin{array}{c} 6 \\ \circled{60} \end{array} = 39$

5. $17 + \begin{array}{c} 2 \\ \circled{20} \end{array} = 37$ 6. $11 + \begin{array}{c} 8 \\ \circled{80} \end{array} = 91$

Writing and Reasoning In Exercise 1, how did you decide which addend was correct?

Possible answer: I compared the first addend and the sum. The tens digit went up by 3. So I knew 3 tens or 30 was added.

Chapter Resources   8-14   Enrich
© Houghton Mifflin Harcourt Publishing Company

Model and Draw

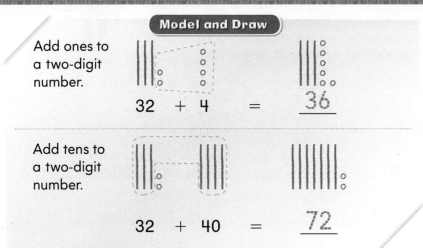

Add ones to a two-digit number.

$$32 + 4 = \underline{36}$$

Add tens to a two-digit number.

$$32 + 40 = \underline{72}$$

Share and Show

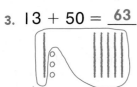

Use ▦. Draw to show how to add the ones. Write the sum. **Possible drawings shown.**

1. $27 + 2 = \underline{29}$

2. $41 + 5 = \underline{46}$

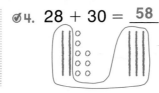

Use ▦. Draw to show how to add the tens. Write the sum. **Possible drawings shown.**

3. $13 + 50 = \underline{63}$

4. $28 + 30 = \underline{58}$

© Houghton Mifflin Harcourt Publishing Company

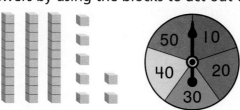

3 EXPLAIN

Model and Draw

MP4 Model with mathematics. Work through the two models with children. Have children first use base-ten blocks to model each addend and then relate their models to the quick pictures and numbers.

• **Look at 32 + 4. Do you need to add tens to find the sum? Why or Why not?** No. There are only 4 ones to add to 32. You just have to add the ones to find the sum.

• **Look at 32 + 40. How does knowing the basic fact 3 + 4 = 7 help you find the sum?** 3 ones plus 4 ones equals 7 ones, so 3 tens plus 4 tens equals 7 tens.

Share and Show

Have children model each exercise with base-ten blocks and then draw to find the sum.

• **How does drawing help you find the sum?** Possible answer: It is easy to see if I need to add ones or tens.

• **How do you know your answer is correct?** Possible answer: I can count the tens and ones in the drawings to be sure they match my answer.

Use the checked exercises for **Quick Check.**

 Quick Check

If ▶ a child misses the checked exercises

Then ▶ **Differentiate Instruction** with
• Reteach 8.5
• Personal Math Trainer 1.NBT.C.4
• RtI Tier 1 Activity (online)

⚠ COMMON ERRORS

Error Children may reverse digits in two-digit addends.

Example In Exercise 2, children may model 14 instead of 41.

Springboard to Learning Have children underline the two-digit addend and check that their drawing matches the correct number of tens and ones before finding the sum.

④ ELABORATE

On Your Own

MP4 Model with mathematics. If children completed Exercises 2 and 4 correctly, assign Exercises 5–14.

 GO DEEPER

MP2 Reason abstractly and quantitatively.
Exercises 13 and 14 require children to apply what they know about adding ones or tens to a two-digit number to choose two addends that make a sum of 45 according to the rule given. Be sure children understand the different rules for each exercise before they do each one.

GO DEEPER

MP7 Look for and make use of structure.
Challenge children to find additional number sentences that match each rule.

- **Suppose you wrote 44 + 1 = 45 for Exercise 13. What is another number sentence you can write that uses the same numbers?**
  I can write 1 + 44 = 45.

MP2 Reason abstractly and quantitatively.

- **What is the greatest number of tens you can add to a two-digit number to get a sum of 45?** 3 tens

---

Name _____

 On Your Own

MATHEMATICAL PRACTICE ④   Use Models

Use ▭▭▭▭ and your MathBoard.
Add the ones or tens. Write the sum.

5. 65 + 3 = __68__   6. 81 + 8 = __89__

7. 54 + 20 = __74__   8. 32 + 10 = __42__

9. 95 + 2 = __97__   10. 25 + 60 = __85__

11. 2 + 54 = __56__   12. 70 + 29 = __99__

GO DEEPER   Make a sum of 45. Draw a quick picture. Write the number sentence.

13. Add ones to a two-digit number.

Possible answer shown. Check that children's drawing matches their number sentence.

__44__ + __1__ = 45

14. Add tens to a two-digit number.

Possible answer shown. Check that children's drawing matches their number sentence.

__25__ + __20__ = 45

Chapter 8 • Lesson 5   four hundred sixty-three   **463**

PROBLEM TYPE SITUATIONS

Addition and Subtraction

Add To • Result Unknown
Exercises: 15, 16

Put Together/Take Apart
Exercise: 17

Common Core **MATHEMATICAL PRACTICES** ANALYZE • LOOK FOR STRUCTURE • PRECISION

Problem Solving • Applications   WRITE Math

Choose a way to solve. Draw or write to show your work.

Check children's work.

15. Rita picks 63 strawberries. Then she picks 30 more. How many strawberries does Rita pick?

___93___ strawberries

16. **THINK SMARTER** Kenny planted two rows of corn. He used 20 seeds in each row. He has 18 seeds left. How many seeds of corn did Kenny have?

___58___ seeds

17. There are 7 oak trees and 32 pine trees in the park. How many trees are in the park?

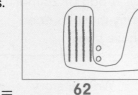

___39___ trees

18. **THINK SMARTER** Use the model. Draw to show how to add the tens.

42 + 20 = ___62___

Check children's drawings. Possible drawing shown.

 TAKE HOME ACTIVITY • Give your child the addition problems 25 + 3 and 25 + 30. Ask your child to explain how to solve each problem.

464 four hundred sixty-four

© Houghton Mifflin Harcourt Publishing Company • Image Credits: (b) ©Alamy; (t) ©PhotoAlto/Getty Images

---

 **DIFFERENTIATED INSTRUCTION** **INDEPENDENT ACTIVITIES**

Grab and Go!
Differentiated Centers Kit

Activities
Count On

Children complete blue Activity Card 20 by counting on to add two-digit numbers.

Literature
It's a Home Run!

Children read the book and add baseball cards.

Games
Neighborhood Sums

Children practice and review sums to 20.

Problem Solving • Applications

Common Core **MATHEMATICAL PRACTICES**

MP6 Attend to precision. Have children complete Exercises 15-17. Have base-ten blocks available if children need them.

THINK SMARTER

MP2 Reason abstractly and quantitatively. Exercise 16 is a multi-step problem. In the first step, children must find how many seeds are planted in two rows. Then children must add 18 to that number to find the total number of seeds Kenny started with. Encourage children to draw quick pictures to help them find the total number of seeds.

   Math on the Spot Video Tutor
Use this video to help children model and solve this type of *Think Smarter* problem.

GO DIGITAL **Math on the Spot** videos are in the Interactive Student Edition and at *www.thinkcentral.com.*

THINK SMARTER

In Exercise 18, children should be able to recognize that adding 20 is the same as adding 2 tens. An answer of 44 indicates that children interpreted the drawing of 2 **tens** as 2 **ones.** For children who struggle to make the quick drawing for the solution, have them circle and count all of the tens to get started.

5 EVALUATE Formative Assessment

Essential Question

Reflect Using the Language Objective Have children listen to a partner explain, and then rephrase in their own words to answer the Essential Question.

How can models help you add ones or tens to a two-digit number? Possible answer: Modeling the addends with base-ten blocks helps me see that I add tens to tens and ones to ones.

Math Journal  WRITE Math

Write a story problem about 40 apples and 17 pears.

Practice and Homework

Use the Practice and Homework pages to provide children with more practice of the concepts and skills presented in this lesson. Children master their understanding as they complete practice items and then challenge their critical thinking skills with Problem Solving. Use the Write Math section to determine children's understanding of content for this lesson. Encourage children to use their Math Journals to record their answers.

Name _____

Use Models to Add

Use ▭▭▭▭▭▭ ▭ and your MathBoard.
Add the ones or tens. Write the sum.

1. $44 + 5 = \underline{49}$

2. $16 + 70 = \underline{86}$

3. $78 + 20 = \underline{98}$

4. $52 + 7 = \underline{59}$

5. $2 + 13 = \underline{15}$

6. $73 + 4 = \underline{77}$

7. $65 + 3 = \underline{68}$

8. $20 + 25 = \underline{45}$

9. $49 + 30 = \underline{79}$

10. $81 + 8 = \underline{89}$

Problem Solving (Real World)

Solve. Draw or write to explain.   Check children's work.

11. Maria has 21 marbles.
She buys a bag of 20 marbles.
How many marbles does
Maria have now?

$21 + 20 = 41$

$\underline{41}$ marbles

12. **WRITE** Math Write a story problem about 40 apples and 17 pears.

Check children's work.

_____

_____

_____

Chapter 8   four hundred sixty-five **465**

© Houghton Mifflin Harcourt Publishing Company

Common Core PROFESSIONAL DEVELOPMENT **Math Talk in Action**

After completing Exercises 1–10, discuss adding ones or tens to a two-digit number.

Teacher: In Exercise 7, what is the first number you modeled?

Sydney: I modeled 65.

Teacher: How many tens did you show? How many ones?

Sydney: 6 tens and 5 ones

Teacher: Good. What if you showed 5 tens and 6 ones?

Mia: That is not right! It would not be the right answer.

Teacher: Why not?

Mia: Because they are not the same numbers. 65 is greater than 56.

Teacher: You are right. How do you find the sum for $65 + 3$?

Ben: I add the 3 ones to 65.

Cho: I add the 3 ones to the 5 ones to get 8 ones. Then I add the 8 ones to 60 to get 68.

Teacher: Those are both good ways to find the sum. You can use a way that makes sense to you.

I. What is the sum?
Write the number.

$$62 + 30 = \underline{92}$$

2. What is the sum?
Write the number.

$$37 + 2 = \underline{39}$$

Spiral Review (1.OA.C.6, 1.NBT.A.1)

3. Write two ways to make 15.

$$\underline{} + \underline{} = 15$$

$$\underline{} + \underline{} = 15$$

Possible answers: 0, 15; 1, 14; 2, 13; 3, 12; 4, 11; 5, 10; 6, 9; 7, 8; 8, 7; 9, 6; 10, 5; 11, 4; 12, 3; 13, 2; 14, 1; 15, 0

4. What number does the model show?

  $\underline{103}$

FOR MORE PRACTICE
GO TO THE
Personal Math Trainer

Continue concepts and skills practice with Lesson Check. Use Spiral Review to engage children in previously taught concepts and to promote content retention. Common Core standards are correlated to each section.

Hands On • Make Ten to Add

LESSON AT A GLANCE

FOCUS **COHERENCE** **RIGOR**

F C R Focus:

Common Core State Standards

■ **1.NBT.C.4** Add within 100, including adding a two-digit number and a one-digit number, and adding a two-digit number and a multiple of 10, using concrete models or drawings and strategies based on place value, properties of operations, and/or the relationship between addition and subtraction; relate the strategy to a written method and explain the reasoning used. Understand that in adding two-digit numbers, one adds tens and tens, ones and ones; and sometimes it is necessary to compose a ten.

MATHEMATICAL PRACTICES (See *Mathematical Practices in GO Math!* in the *Planning Guide* for full text.)
MP2 Reason abstractly and quantitatively. **MP5** Use appropriate tools strategically.

F C R Coherence:

Standards Across the Grades
Before	Grade 1	After
K.NBT.A.1	1.NBT.C.4	2.NBT.B.5

F C R Rigor:

Level 1: Understand Concepts....................*Share and Show* (✓ Checked Items)
Level 2: Procedural Skills and Fluency.......*On Your Own, Practice and Homework*
Level 3: Applications................................*Think Smarter and Go Deeper*

Learning Objective
Make a ten to add a two-digit number and a one-digit number.

Language Objective
Children write in their Math Journal one reason how making a ten can help you add a two-digit number and a one-digit number.

Materials
MathBoard, base-ten blocks

F C R For more about how *GO Math!* fosters **Coherence** within the Content Standards and Mathematical Progressions for this chapter, see page 433J.

About the Math
Professional Development

Progress to Algebra
If Children Ask

"What is the right way to add?" is a question some children may ask when encouraged to use different methods to solve addition. The answer is that there are many "right" ways to add.

When adding two-digit numbers, many learners prefer to start with the bigger part of the number and then add the smaller parts. Mathematically, there is no reason that children should not add the tens before adding the ones.

If children are working with numbers where there are 10 or more ones in the sum, the same informal rules apply. After combining the tens, have children combine the ones. Then they can add the two parts together.

Children may develop a deeper understanding of how numbers compose and decompose when encouraged to master a way of adding that makes sense to them.

 Professional Development Videos

 GO DIGITAL

SE Interactive Student Edition

Personal Math Trainer

Math on the Spot Video

Animated Math Models

iT iTools: Base-Ten Blocks

MM HMH Mega Math

Problem of the Day 8.6

Calendar Math Find the third Sunday of the month. Count on five days. What is the date? Answer depends on the month being used.

 As time allows, solve similar problems where children count on ones from a two-digit number.

Vocabulary

 • Interactive Student Edition
• Multimedia eGlossary

Fluency Builder
I Am Thinking of a Number

You can use this game to review tens and ones.

Have children listen to the first clue. They use their MathBoard to record possible answers. Then read the second clue. Children circle the number that fits both clues.

I am thinking of a number that has fewer than 4 tens and more than 2 tens. It has one more one than it has tens.

30	31	32	33	(34)
35	36	37	38	39

Repeat the activity with other two-clue examples. Encourage children to name numbers that fit the first clue, and explain how they used the second clue to eliminate possible answers.

❶ ENGAGE

with the Interactive Student Edition

Essential Question
How can making a ten help you add a two-digit number and a one-digit number?

Making Connections
Lead a discussion to focus children on sharing what they know about the "make a ten" strategy.

- **When is it helpful to use the "make a ten" strategy?** When I want to add two numbers and I can use ones from one number to make a ten.

Learning Activity
What problem are children trying to solve? Connect the story to the problem. Ask the following questions.

- **When you use the "make a ten" strategy, what must you remember to do with the ones you combined to make a ten?** I must think of the group of ones as one ten.

- **How does your model change after you make a ten?** My model shows one more ten and fewer ones.

Literacy and Mathematics
Invite children to write a story about how to add a two-digit number and a one-digit number. Then have partners read and compare stories.

2 EXPLORE

Listen and Draw

Materials base-ten blocks

Read the following problem aloud as children listen attentively.

Sally has 21 stickers in her sticker book. She gets 6 more stickers. How many stickers does Sally have now? 27 stickers

Have children use base-ten blocks to model the addends and find the sum.

- **How can you show 21 and 6 using tens and ones?** I make a group of 2 tens and 1 one to show 21. I make another group of 6 ones to show 6.

- **How can the model help you add 21 and 6?** Possible answer: I see that I can add the ones from both numbers. There are 7 ones. Then I count the tens. There are 2 tens, or 20. So 20 + 7 = 27.

- **How can you draw to show the addition?** Possible answer: I can draw quick pictures to show a group of 2 tens, 1 one and a group of 6 ones. I draw a circle around all the ones to show they are added together.

 **MP5 Use appropriate tools strategically.** Use Math Talk to focus on children's understanding of adding tens and ones using a model.

- **How would your model change if Sally started with 31 stickers?** Possible answer: I would show three tens and one one for 31, and my answer would change to 37.

MP2 Reason abstractly and quantitatively.

- **Why did you circle all the ones?** Possible answer: to show how many ones in all.

 Strategy:
Understand Context

Use base-ten blocks to build understanding in context.

Write **26 + 7 = _____**. Show the problem with base-ten blocks. Explain how to make ten to find the sum.

- **First I think about how many more ones I need to make 30. I need four more.** Take 4 ones from 7 and the 6 ones from 26 and exchange them for a tens block. Now **I have 30 and 3 more. 26 + 7 = 33.**

Point out that 10 ones blocks can be exchanged for 1 tens block.

1.NBT.C.4 Add within 100, including adding a two-digit number and a one-digit number, and adding a two-digit number and a multiple of 10, using concrete models or drawings and strategies based on place value, properties of operations, and/or the relationship between addition and subtraction; relate the strategy to a written method and explain the reasoning used. Understand that in adding two-digit numbers, one adds tens and tens, ones and ones; and sometimes it is necessary to compose a ten.

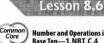 Progress to Algebra

Name _____

Make Ten to Add

Essential Question How can making a ten help you add a two-digit number and a one-digit number?

HANDS ON
Lesson 8.6

Common Core · **Number and Operations in Base Ten—1.NBT.C.4**
MATHEMATICAL PRACTICES
MP2, MP5

 Listen and Draw

Use ▭. Draw to show how you can find the sum.

Possible drawing shown.

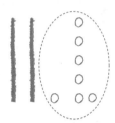

$$21 + 6 = \underline{27}.$$

Malk Talk: Possible answer: I use tens and ones to show the numbers 21 and 6. I add all the tens and ones together to get a sum of 2 tens and 7 ones, or 27.

Problem Type:
Add To • Result Unknown

FOR THE TEACHER • Read the following problem. Sally has 21 stickers in her sticker book. She gets 6 more stickers. How many stickers does Sally have now?

Math Talk MATHEMATICAL PRACTICES 5

Use Tools Explain how your model shows the sum of 21 + 6.

Chapter 8

four hundred sixty-seven **467**

Reteach 8.6 ▲ RtI

Name _____

Lesson 8.6
Reteach

Make Ten to Add

What is 17 + 5?
Step 1
Use ●.
Show 17.
Use ○.
Show 5.

Step 2
Make a ten.

Step 3 Add.

20 + 2 = _22_

So, 17 + 5 = _22_

Draw to show how you make a ten. Find the sum.
1. What is 16 + 8?

_20_ + _4_ = _24_

So, 16 + 8 = _24_

Chapter Resources
© Houghton Mifflin Harcourt Publishing Company

8-15

Reteach

Enrich 8.6 Differentiated Instruction

Name _____

Lesson 8.6
Enrich

Berry Easy Addition

Add. Circle the strawberries that have the same sum.

1. 25 + 8 = _33_
2. 30 + 6 = _36_
3. 27 + 9 = _36_
4. 29 + 7 = _36_
5. 31 + 4 = _35_

Writing and Reasoning Explain how you could make the other strawberries match the sum.

Possible answer: Add 3 more to Exercise 1.

Add 1 more to Exercise 5.

Chapter Resources
© Houghton Mifflin Harcourt Publishing Company

8-16

Enrich

Model and Draw

Make a ten to find 37 + 8.

What can I add to 7 to make 10?

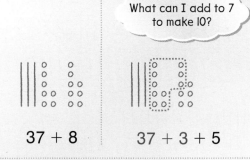

37 + 8   37 + 3 + 5   40 + 5

$\underline{40} + \underline{5} = \underline{45}$

So, 37 + 8 = $\underline{45}$.

Share and Show MATH BOARD

Use ▭. Draw to show how you make a ten. Find the sum.

☑ 1. 49 + 3 = ?

Children's circling may vary.

$\underline{50} + \underline{2} = \underline{52}$

So, 49 + 3 = $\underline{52}$.

468 four hundred sixty-eight

© Houghton Mifflin Harcourt Publishing Company

Advanced Learners

Logical / Mathematical
Small Group

Materials index cards

- Have each child choose a number from 1 to 9 and another number from 10 to 90, and write each number on separate index cards.

- Collect the cards to make a group of one-digit number cards and a group of two-digit number cards. Have a volunteer take a card from each group and find the sum.

- Have the child continue to take a one-digit card and add the number to the previous sum until they must make a ten to add. Have them record the numbers they added.

- Give each child an opportunity to choose cards and make a ten to add. Then lead a discussion about why some children had to take more cards than others.

---

3 EXPLAIN

Model and Draw Common Core MATHEMATICAL PRACTICES

MP5 Use appropriate tools strategically. Guide children through the model at the top of the page. Have them use base-ten blocks to model the process, grouping the ones to make a ten.

- **How do you know how many ones to add to 37 to make a 10?** Possible answer: 37 has 7 ones. I know that 7 + 3 = 10. So, I need to add 3 ones to 7 ones to make a 10.

- **What is the sum?** 3 tens plus 1 ten plus 5 ones is the same as 4 tens plus 5 ones, or 45.

- **Why does thinking about tens and ones help in solving the addition?** Possible answer: When I have 10 or more ones in all, I can make another ten. When I know the total number of tens and ones, I can quickly write the sum.

Share and Show MATH BOARD

Have children use their MathBoards and base-ten blocks to solve Exercise 1 and draw to show how they make a ten.

- **How do you know your answer is correct?** Possible answer: I counted the ones and knew I had more than ten ones so I made a ten. I added the ten to the tens I already had to get 50. Then I counted my ones and added them to 50 to show 52.

Use the checked exercise for **Quick Check.**

✔ Quick Check ▲ RtI

If	a child misses the checked exercises

Then	**Differentiate Instruction** with • Reteach 8.6 • Personal Math Trainer 1.NBT.C.4 • RtI Tier 1 Activity (online)

! COMMON ERRORS

Error Children may simply add all the ones together and then combine the digits.

Example In Exercise 1, children write 40 + 12 = 412.

Springboard to Learning Remind children to make a ten when they can. They will now have one more ten than they started with.

Lesson 8.6 468

On Your Own

MP5 Use appropriate tools strategically. If children answered Exercise 1 correctly, assign Exercises 2–6. Remind children to show how they make a ten.

 THINK SMARTER

Exercises 5 and 6 require children to use higher order thinking skills as they decompose the one-digit number for the purpose of composing a ten.

Math on the Spot Video Tutor

Use this video to help children model and solve this type of *Think Smarter* problem.

 Math on the Spot videos are in the Interactive Student Edition and at *www.thinkcentral.com*.

GO DEEPER

MP7 Look for and make use of structure. To extend learning, have children look back at Exercises 5 and 6 and find other ways they can use ones to make a ten. Have children share their ideas by writing on the board. For example, 46 + 7 may also be solved by decomposing 46 as shown below.

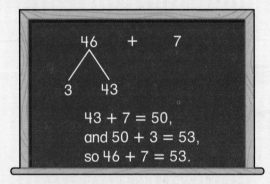

MP2 Reason abstractly and quantitatively.

- **How does thinking about the addends in different ways help you solve the problem?**
  Possible answer: I can group numbers in ways that make sense. For example, I can regroup one number to make a ten.

Name _____

On Your Own

MATHEMATICAL PRACTICE ⑤ Use a Concrete Model

Use ▭▭▭▭▭ ▯. Draw to show how you make a ten. Find the sum.

2. $39 + 7 =$ __46__

Children's circling may vary.

3. $72 + 9 =$ __81__

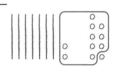

4. $58 + 5 =$ __63__

THINK SMARTER Solve. Write the numbers.

5. 46 + 7

$46 + \boxed{4} + 3$

$\boxed{50} + 3$

So, $46 + 7 =$ __53__.

6. 53 + 8

$53 + \boxed{7} + 1$

$\boxed{60} + 1$

So, $53 + 8 =$ __61__.

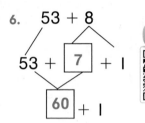
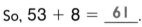

PROBLEM TYPE SITUATIONS

Addition and Subtraction

Add To • Result Unknown
Exercise: 7

Take From • Result Unknown
Exercise: 8

Problem Solving • Applications   WRITE Math

Choose a way to solve. Draw or write to show your work.

Check children's work.

7. **THINK SMARTER** Koby puts 24 daisies and 8 tulips in a vase. How many flowers are in the vase?

_____32_____ flowers

8. **GO DEEPER** There are 27 ducklings in the water. 20 of them come out of the water. How many ducklings are still in the water?

_____7_____ ducklings

9. Write the missing addend.

$$46 + \boxed{6} = 52$$

10. **THINK SMARTER** Use the model. Draw to show how to make a ten.

 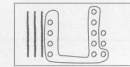 

34   +   8   =   42

Check children's drawings. Possible drawing shown.

 TAKE HOME ACTIVITY • Ask your child to explain how to find the sum for 25 + 9.

470 four hundred seventy

© Houghton Mifflin Harcourt Publishing Company • Image Credits: (tc) ©PhotoDisc/Getty Images; (bc) ©Getty Images

---

DIFFERENTIATED INSTRUCTION   INDEPENDENT ACTIVITIES

Grab-and-Go!
Differentiated Centers Kit

Activities
Regroup

Children complete orange Activity Card 20 by modeling addition of two-digit numbers with regrouping.

Literature
It's a Homerun!

Children read the book and add baseball cards.

Games
Flying Along

Children practice 2-digit addition with regrouping.

Problem Solving • Applications

THINK SMARTER

MP2 Reason abstractly and quantitatively. Have children read Exercise 7. Ask them to describe how they will solve the problem.

GO DEEPER

Exercise 8 challenges children to think addition to subtract.

THINK SMARTER

Exercise 10 assesses whether children can make a ten to add a two-digit number and a one-digit number when the addition involves more than 9 ones. Children who answer incorrectly may not be able to reason quantitatively and apply a proper math technique to solve. Have children count the unit cubes and circle 10 of them to begin their solutions.

5 EVALUATE Formative Assessment

Essential Question

Reflect Using the Language Objective Have children write in their Math Journal one supporting reason to help answer the Essential Question.

How can making a ten help you add a two-digit number and a one-digit number?

Possible answer: When I draw all the tens and ones, I can write that number as the sum.

Math Journal Math

Use words or pictures to explain how to solve 44 + 7.

Practice and Homework

Use the Practice and Homework pages to provide children with more practice of the concepts and skills presented in this lesson. Children master their understanding as they complete practice items and then challenge their critical thinking skills with Problem Solving. Use the Write Math section to determine children's understanding of content for this lesson. Encourage children to use their Math Journals to record their answers.

Make Ten to Add

 COMMON CORE STANDARD—1.NBT.C.4
Use place value understanding and properties of operations to add and subtract.

Use . Draw to show how you make a ten. Find the sum.

Other ways are possible. Check children's drawings.

1. $26 + 5 =$ __31__

2. $68 + 4 =$ __72__

Problem Solving Real World

Choose a way to solve. Draw or write to show your work.

Check children's work.

3. Debbie has 27 markers. Sal has 9 markers. How many markers do they have?

$27 + 9 = 36$

__36__ markers

4. WRITE Math Use words or pictures to explain how to solve $44 + 7$.

Check children's work.

© Houghton Mifflin Harcourt Publishing Company

Cross-Curricular   S.T.E.M.

Materials pictures of baby and adult animals

- Have children match pictures of young animals to pictures of adult animals. For example, children may match hen to chick, cat to kitten, and cow to calf. Discuss the differences and similarities between each young animal and its adult form.

- Have children write and share story problems in which they add a two-digit and a one-digit number. For example:

  A hen has 9 chicks. Another hen has 12 chicks. How many chicks are there? 21 chicks

SOCIAL STUDIES

- Explain that people sometimes put their money into a bank to save or to keep safely.

- Have children solve problems about saving money. For example:

  Carol has 25 dollars in the bank. She puts 7 more dollars in the bank. How many dollars does Carol have in the bank now? 32 dollars

1. What is the sum?
   Write the number.

$$47 + 6 = \underline{53}$$

2. What is the sum?
   Write the number.

$$84 + 8 = \underline{92}$$

3. What number does the
   model show?
   Write the number.

 $\underline{114}$

4. Write a number to make the sentence true.

$$5 + 4 = 10 - \underline{1}$$

FOR MORE PRACTICE
GO TO THE
Personal Math Trainer

© Houghton Mifflin Harcourt Publishing Company

Continue concepts and skills practice with Lesson Check. Use Spiral Review to engage children in previously taught concepts and to promote content retention. Common Core standards are correlated to each section.

Hands On • Use Place Value to Add

LESSON AT A GLANCE

FOCUS   COHERENCE   RIGOR

F C R Focus:

Common Core State Standards

1.NBT.C.4 Add within 100, including adding a two-digit number and a one-digit number, and adding a two-digit number and a multiple of 10, using concrete models or drawings and strategies based on place value, properties of operations, and/or the relationship between addition and subtraction; relate the strategy to a written method and explain the reasoning used. Understand that in adding two-digit numbers, one adds tens and tens, ones and ones; and sometimes it is necessary to compose a ten.

MATHEMATICAL PRACTICES (See *Mathematical Practices in GO Math!* in the *Planning Guide* for full text.)
MP1 Make sense of problems and persevere in solving them. **MP2** Reason abstractly and quantitatively. **MP6** Attend to precision. **MP7** Look for and make use of structure.

F C R Coherence:

Standards Across the Grades
Before   Grade 1   After
K.NBT.A.1   1.NBT.C.4   2.NBT.B.5

F C R Rigor:

Level 1: Understand Concepts...................*Share and Show* (✓ Checked Items)
Level 2: Procedural Skills and Fluency.......*On Your Own, Practice and Homework*
Level 3: Applications...............................*Think Smarter and Go Deeper*

Learning Objective
Use tens and ones to add two-digit numbers.

Language Objective
Child teams present to the class how can you model tens and ones to help you add two-digit numbers.

Materials
MathBoard, base-ten blocks

F C R For more about how *GO Math!* fosters **Coherence** within the Content Standards and Mathematical Progressions for this chapter, see page 433J.

About the Math
Professional Development

Progress to Algebra
Why Teach This

In this lesson, children model the tens and ones in two-digit numbers to add. It is important for children to learn this approach to multi-digit addition so they have a better understanding of the meaning of addition.

If children only learn the standard addition algorithm, they may be at a loss when they start regrouping in addition. The process of grouping 10 ones for 1 ten becomes a rote action without meaning. Children will begin to see that the ones, when added, may produce a two-digit number. The little carried number is not used until later with the standard algorithm when its meaning becomes clear.

Learning to model numbers as tens and ones to add the tens and ones can help children develop mental math skills. Children can create strategies to add the numbers in their head.

 Professional Development Videos

 GO DIGITAL

 **Interactive Student Edition**

 **Personal Math Trainer**

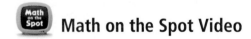 **Math on the Spot Video**

 **Animated Math Models**

iT *iTools:* Base-Ten Blocks

Daily Routines
Common Core

 Problem of the Day 8.7

Word of the Day ones
Write a number that has 6 ones.
Write a number that has no ones.
Possible answers: 16; 50

If time allows, continue the activity.
You may invite volunteers to ask similar
questions.

Vocabulary

GO DIGITAL
• **Interactive Student Edition**
• **Multimedia eGlossary**

 Fluency Builder
Making Numbers

Materials index cards

Arrange for children to work in small
groups. Give each group 20 index cards.
On 10 of the cards, children write 0 tens,
1 ten, 2 tens, and so on, up to 9 tens. On the
remaining 10 cards, children write 0 ones,
1 one, 2 ones, and so on, up to 9 ones.

Have groups shuffle each set of cards and
put them facedown in separate piles.
Taking turns, each child chooses a card from
each pile and uses both cards to write the
number described.

Continue the activity until all cards have
been used.

❶ ENGAGE

with the Interactive Student Edition

Essential Question
How can you model tens and ones to help you add
two-digit numbers?

Making Connections
Ask children to tell what they know about two-digit numbers.

- **What does 7 in the number 27 mean?** 7 ones
- **What does 2 in the number 27 mean?** 2 tens
- **What does this tell you about two-digit numbers?** Possible answer:
  The ones are always on the left and the tens are always on the right.

Learning Activity
What problem are children trying to solve? Connect the story to the
problem. Ask the following questions.

- **When you add two-digit numbers, why is it important to line
  up the numbers in columns?** Possible answer: So I can see the ones
  together and the tens together.
- **What happens if your model has more than ten ones in the ones
  column?** Possible answer: You can make a ten. **How do you show this
  change?** You trade ten ones for one ten and put that ten in the tens
  column.

Literacy and Mathematics
Choose from one or more of the following activities.

- Say a two-digit number, such as 48, and have children a draw
  quick picture of the number. Then have children say the number
  using this frame: 48 is 4 tens and 8 ones. Repeat with other two-
  digit numbers.
- Have children restate the problem and explain how they would
  model to solve the problem.

② EXPLORE

Listen and Draw

Materials. base-ten blocks

Read the following problem aloud. Have children model with base-ten blocks on the Tens and Ones mat and then draw to show their work.

Cameron has 30 new stamps and 25 old stamps. How many stamps does Cameron have?

- **How did you model 30 on the mat?** I put 3 tens blocks in the Tens column at the top of the mat.

- **What did you put in the Ones column? Explain.** Possible answer: I did not show any ones because 30 has 3 tens and no ones.

- **How did you model 25?** Possible answer: I put 2 tens blocks in the Tens column and 5 ones blocks in the Ones column at the bottom of the mat.

- **How can Cameron add the tens and ones blocks to find the sum?** Possible answer: He can add the ones to ones and the tens to tens.

- **What is the sum?** 55 **How do you know?** There are 5 tens and 5 ones in the sum.

 MP1 Make sense of problems and persevere in solving them. Use Math Talk to focus on children's understanding of adding tens to tens and ones to ones when adding two-digit numbers.

- **How do the columns help you model the problem?** They help keep my work organized. They help me group the ones and the tens.

ELL Strategy:
Illustrate Understanding

Have children work in pairs to illustrate 2-digit addition.

Write **25 + 17 = ____**.

Ask pairs of children to draw lines and dots to represent the problem. Have the pairs work together to solve the problem.

Ask each pair of children to explain why their answer is correct. Help them with vocabulary as needed.

MP7 Look for and make use of structure.

- **How is your drawing like a two-digit number?** The ones are on the right and the tens are on the left in my drawing, just like in a two-digit number.

Progress to Algebra

1.NBT.C.4 Add within 100, including adding a two-digit number and a one-digit number, and adding a two-digit number and a multiple of 10, using concrete models or drawings and strategies based on place value, properties of operations, and/ or the relationship between addition and subtraction; relate the strategy to a written method and explain the reasoning used. Understand that in adding two-digit numbers, one adds tens and tens, ones and ones; and sometimes it is necessary to compose a ten.

Name _____

Use Place Value to Add

Essential Question How can you model tens and ones to help you add two-digit numbers?

HANDS ON
Lesson 8.7

Common Core · **Number and Operations in Base Ten—1.NBT.C.4**
MATHEMATICAL PRACTICES
MP1, MP2, MP6, MP7

Listen and Draw

Model the problem with .
Draw a quick picture to show your work.

Tens	Ones
||| |||	○ ○ ○ ○ ○

Math Talk: Possible answer: 3 tens and 2 tens equal 5 tens. 0 ones and 5 ones equal 5 ones. There are 5 tens and 5 ones in all, or 55.

FOR THE TEACHER • Read the following problem. Cameron has 30 old stamps and 25 new stamps. How many stamps does Cameron have?

Chapter 8   **Problem Type:**
Put Together/Take Apart • Total Unknown

Math Talk MATHEMATICAL PRACTICES

Describe How many tens? How many ones? How many in all?

four hundred seventy-three **473**

Reteach 8.7   ▲ RtI

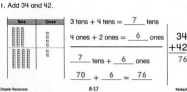

Enrich 8.7   **Differentiated Instruction**

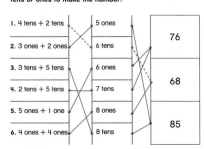

Model and Draw

How can you use tens and ones to add?

$$\begin{array}{r} 35 \\ +38 \\ \hline \end{array}$$

Tens	Ones

$$\begin{array}{r} 3 \text{ tens} + 5 \text{ ones} \\ 3 \text{ tens} + 8 \text{ ones} \\ \hline \underline{6}\ \text{tens} + \underline{13}\ \text{ones} \end{array}$$

$$60 + 13 = 73$$

$$\begin{array}{r} 35 \\ +38 \\ \hline 73 \end{array}$$

Share and Show MATH BOARD

Draw a quick picture.
Use tens and ones to add.

☑ I.

Tens	Ones

$$\begin{array}{r} 81 \\ +14 \\ \hline \end{array}$$

$$\begin{array}{r} 8 \text{ tens} + 1 \text{ one} \\ 1 \text{ ten} + 4 \text{ ones} \\ \hline \underline{9}\ \text{tens} + \underline{5}\ \text{ones} \end{array}$$

$$90 + 5 = 95$$

$$\begin{array}{r} 81 \\ +14 \\ \hline 95 \end{array}$$

Advanced Learners Visual / Kinesthetic Individual / Partners

Materials distinct markers (for example, button or penny) Hundred Chart, 10-section Spinner (see *eTeacher Resources*), paper clip, pencil

- Label the spinner with the numbers 0, 10, 20, 30, 40, 50, 60, 70, 80, and 90.

- Show children how to spin the spinner using a pencil and the paper clip. Have children each place their marker on a different number in the first row of the Hundred Chart.

- Children take turns spinning the spinner. They should count on by tens the number spun, and move their counter to the sum. The first child to go over 100 wins.

1	2	3	4	5	6	7	8	9	10
11	12	13	14	15	16	17	18	19	20
21	22	23	24	25	26	27	28	29	30
31	32	33	34	35	36	37	38	39	40
41	42	43	44	45	46	47	48	49	50
51	52	53	54	55	56	57	58	59	60
61	62	63	64	65	66	67	68	69	70

---

③ EXPLAIN

Model and Draw Common Core MATHEMATICAL PRACTICES

MP7 Look for and make use of structure. Guide children through the model at the top of the page with the following questions.

- **How can you show the tens and ones for the numbers 35 and 38?** Possible answer: I can draw 3 lines to show 3 tens and 5 circles to show 5 ones in 35. I can draw 3 lines to show 3 tens and 8 circles to show 8 ones in 38.

- **How do you find the sum?** Possible answer: I add the tens to the tens and the ones to the ones. Then I add the total number of tens to the total number of ones.

- **How do you add 60 + 13?** Possible answer: I add the parts as 60 + 10 = 70, and 70 + 3 = 73.

Ask children to use their MathBoard to show other ways to solve 35 + 38. Invite volunteers to show their solutions.

Share and Show MATH BOARD

- **How do you know your answer is correct?** Possible answer: I can use my drawing to check my answer. I can compare to be sure that I have the same number of ones and the same number of tens in each model.

Use the checked exercise for **Quick Check**.

✔ **Quick Check** RtI

If a child misses the checked exercise

Then **Differentiate Instruction with**
- Reteach 8.7
- Personal Math Trainer 1.NBT.C.4
- RtI Tier 1 Activity (online)

⚠ COMMON ERRORS

Error Children may add the number of tens to the number of ones.

Example For Exercise 1, children record ___9___ + ___5___ = ___14___ as the second addition sentence.

Springboard to Learning Tell children that the value of 9 tens is 90 and not 9. To correct this error, have children build both numbers with base-ten blocks.

4 ELABORATE

On Your Own

MP6 Attend to precision. If children answered Exercise 1 correctly, assign Exercises 2–6.

THINK SMARTER

MP7 Look for and make use of structure. Exercises 4 and 5 require children to use higher order thinking skills as they decompose two-digit numbers to simplify addition. One method is to decompose the numbers to make a multiple of ten, such as 20 or 30. In Exercise 5, for example, 28 is close to 30, so 2 ones are taken from 17 to make 30, which leaves 15.

Math on the Spot Video Tutor

Use this video to help children model and solve this type of *Think Smarter* problem.

 Math on the Spot videos are in the Interactive Student Edition and at *www.thinkcentral.com*.

 GO DEEPER

MP3 Construct viable arguments and critique the reasoning of others. To extend learning, allow children to explore other ways to decompose the addends in Exercises 4 and 5. Have children take turns presenting their methods to the class.

MP2 Reason abstractly and quantitatively.

- **Why is it helpful to make a ten when finding the answers to Exercises 4 and 5?** Possible answer: When I make a ten, one of the two-digit numbers ends in 0 and that makes it easier to find how many ones quickly.

THINK SMARTER

Exercise 6 requires children to use higher order thinking skills as they draw a quick picture to solve the word problem.

Name _____

 On Your Own

MATHEMATICAL PRACTICE 6 Make Connections
Draw a quick picture. Use tens and ones to add.

2.
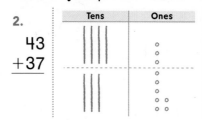

$$43 + 37$$

Tens	Ones

4 tens + 3 ones
3 tens + 7 ones
____7____ tens + __10__ ones
__70__ + __10__ = __80__

$$\begin{array}{r} 43 \\ +37 \\ \hline 80 \end{array}$$

3.
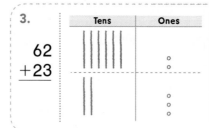

$$62 + 23$$

Tens	Ones

6 tens + 2 ones
2 tens + 3 ones
____8____ tens + __5__ ones
__80__ + __5__ = __85__

$$\begin{array}{r} 62 \\ +23 \\ \hline 85 \end{array}$$

THINK SMARTER Solve.

4. 28 + 17

28 + __2__ + 15

__30__ + 15 = __45__

So, 28 + 17 = __45__.

5. 59 + 13

59 + __1__ + 12

__60__ + 12 = __72__

So, 59 + 13 = __72__.

6. **THINK** SMARTER Draw a quick picture to solve. Han has 37 shells. Jonah has 15 shells. How many shells do they have?
Possible picture shown.   __52__

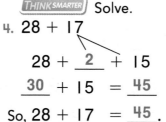

Tens	Ones

Chapter 8 • Lesson 7   four hundred seventy-five **475**

PROBLEM TYPE SITUATION

Addition and Subtraction

Put Together/Take Apart • Total Unknown
Exercises: 6, 7

© Houghton Mifflin Harcourt Publishing Company

Problem Solving • Applications (Real World)

  WRITE) Math

7. **THINK SMARTER** Draw a quick picture to solve. Kim has 24 marbles. Al has 47 marbles. How many marbles do they have?

Possible picture shown.

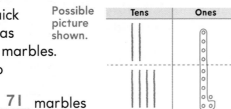

Tens	Ones

___71___ marbles

8. **GO DEEPER** Choose two addends from 11 to 49. Draw them. Add in any order to solve.

Possible answer is shown. Check children's work.

Addend **Addend**

$36 + 43 = 79$

$43 + 36 = 79$

9. **THINK SMARTER** Write the addition that the model shows. Solve.

Tens	Ones

$52 + 15 = 67$

 TAKE HOME ACTIVITY • Write the numbers 42 and 17. Have your child tell how to find the sum by adding the tens and ones.

476 four hundred seventy-six

© Houghton Mifflin Harcourt Publishing Company

DIFFERENTIATED INSTRUCTION **INDEPENDENT ACTIVITIES**

 Grab-and-Go!™

Differentiated Centers Kit

Activities
Neat Trick

Children complete purple Activity Card 20 by using place value and basic facts to add two-digit numbers.

Literature
It's a Homerun!

 Math Readers

Children read the book and add baseball cards.

Games
Flying Along

Games

Children practice 2-digit addition with regrouping.

Problem Solving • Applications (Real World)

Common Core **MATHEMATICAL PRACTICES**

THINK SMARTER

MP6 Attend to precision. Have children read Exercise 7 and tell how they will show the addition.

GO DEEPER

MP7 Look for and make use of structure. Exercise 8 requires children to use the Commutative Property. Children should recall what they learned about *add in any order* to write the two addition sentences.

THINK SMARTER

Exercise 9 assesses whether children can model tens and ones to help them add. Children must first read across the table rather than down in order to identify the two-digit numbers being added. Then they use the table to add down to find the total number of tens and the total number of ones. For children who struggle, add an intermediate step of writing 5 tens + 2 ones above 1 ten + 5 ones.

5 EVALUATE Formative Assessment

Essential Question

Reflect Using the Language Objective Have child teams present to the class to answer the Essential Question.

How can you model tens and ones to help you add two-digit numbers? Possible answer: I add the tens to the tens. I add the ones to the ones. Then I add those numbers to find the sum.

Math Journal  WRITE) Math

Write and solve a story problem to add 12 and 18.

Practice and Homework

Use the Practice and Homework pages to provide children with more practice of the concepts and skills presented in this lesson. Children master their understanding as they complete practice items and then challenge their critical thinking skills with Problem Solving. Use the Write Math section to determine children's understanding of content for this lesson. Encourage children to use their Math Journals to record their answers.

Use Place Value to Add

COMMON CORE STANDARD—1.NBT.C.4
Use place value understanding and properties of operations to add and subtract.

Draw a quick picture. Use tens and ones to add.

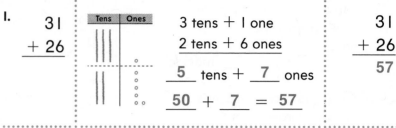

1.
$\begin{array}{r} 31 \\ + 26 \\ \hline \end{array}$

3 tens + 1 one
2 tens + 6 ones

__5__ tens + __7__ ones

__50__ + __7__ = __57__

$\begin{array}{r} 31 \\ + 26 \\ \hline 57 \end{array}$

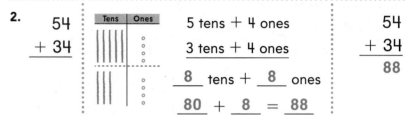

2.
$\begin{array}{r} 54 \\ + 34 \\ \hline \end{array}$

5 tens + 4 ones
3 tens + 4 ones

__8__ tens + __8__ ones

__80__ + __8__ = __88__

$\begin{array}{r} 54 \\ + 34 \\ \hline 88 \end{array}$

Problem Solving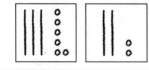

3. Write two addition sentences you can use to find the sum. Then solve.

Addend   **Addend**

__36__ + __22__ = __58__

__22__ + __36__ = __58__

4. WRITE Math Write and solve a story problem to add 12 and 18.

Check children's work.

_____

© Houghton Mifflin Harcourt Publishing Company

Extend the Math   Activity

Making Numbers

Materials chart paper, base-ten blocks, Hundred Chart (see *eTeacher Resources*)

Investigate Have children model, draw, or write as many ways as they can to show the number 43. Remind children that they have learned many ways to make a number. Have children share some of their ways. Record the possible solutions on a piece of chart paper so children can compare their solutions to others.

Math Talk Use the following questions to guide the activity.

Answers will vary. Possible answers are shown.

- **How can you model to make the number 43?** 4 tens 3 ones, 3 tens 13 ones, 2 tens 23 ones, 1 ten 33 ones, 43 ones
- **What would be another way to say 4 tens 3 ones?** 40 + 3

- **Can you add other numbers to show 43?** 10 + 10 + 10 + 10 + 3
- **Did anyone use subtraction?** 53 − 10, 44 − 1
- **What are some strategies you used to come up with different ways?** I wrote 42 + 1. Then I thought of add in any order and wrote 1 + 42.
- **Can there be any more ways to make 43? Why or why not?** Yes. You can combine and break apart models and add and subtract in so many ways. The total number of tens and ones stays the same.

Summarize Children find as many ways as they can to make the number 43.

1. What is the sum?
   Write the number.

   $$
   \begin{array}{r}
   42 \\
   + \, 31 \\
   \hline
   73
   \end{array}
   $$

2. What is the sum?
   Write the number.

   $$
   \begin{array}{r}
   23 \\
   + \, 12 \\
   \hline
   35
   \end{array}
   $$

Spiral Review (1.OA.C.6, 1.NBT.B.2)

3. I have 28 cubes. How many tens and ones can I make?

   Possible answers:

   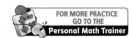

   __2__ tens __8__ ones

   __1__ ten __18__ ones

4. What is the sum?
   Write the number.

   $$
   \begin{array}{r}
   5 \\
   + \, 5 \\
   \hline
   10
   \end{array}
   $$

FOR MORE PRACTICE
GO TO THE
Personal Math Trainer

© Houghton Mifflin Harcourt Publishing Company

Continue concepts and skills practice with Lesson Check. Use Spiral Review to engage children in previously taught concepts and to promote content retention. Common Core standards are correlated to each section.

Problem Solving • Addition Word Problems

LESSON AT A GLANCE

FOCUS   COHERENCE   RIGOR

F C R Focus:

Common Core State Standards

1.NBT.C.4 Add within 100, including adding a two-digit number and a one-digit number, and adding a two-digit number and a multiple of 10, using concrete models or drawings and strategies based on place value, properties of operations, and/or the relationship between addition and subtraction; relate the strategy to a written method and explain the reasoning used. Understand that in adding two-digit numbers, one adds tens and tens, ones and ones; and sometimes it is necessary to compose a ten.

MATHEMATICAL PRACTICES (See *Mathematical Practices in GO Math!* in the *Planning Guide* for full text.)
MP1 Make sense of problems and persevere in solving them. **MP2** Reason abstractly and quantitatively.
MP6 Attend to precision. **MP8** Look for and express regularity in repeated reasoning.

F C R Coherence:

Standards Across the Grades

Before	Grade 1	After
K.NBT.A.1	1.NBT.C.4	2.NBT.B.5

F C R Rigor:

Level 1: Understand Concepts....................*Share and Show* (✓ Checked Items)
Level 2: Procedural Skills and Fluency.......*On Your Own, Practice and Homework*
Level 3: Applications..................................*Think Smarter and Go Deeper*

Learning Objective
Solve and explain two-digit addition word problems using the strategy *draw a picture*.

Language Objective
Child pairs design a poster that demonstrates how drawing a picture can help you explain how to solve an addition problem.

Materials
MathBoard, base-ten blocks, connecting cubes, Hundred Chart (see *eTeacher Resources*)

F C R For more about how *GO Math!* fosters **Coherence** within the Content Standards and Mathematical Progressions for this chapter, see page 433J.

About the Math
Professional Development

Teaching for Depth

Problem-solving lessons can be rich opportunities for building critical thinking skills. Be open to different approaches that children may use, but be sure that they can support their ideas with sound reasoning. Work toward developing a problem-solving community within your classroom.

Presentations followed by discussion are key tools that you can use to help children build a repertoire of problem-solving strategies and skills. For each problem, ask a volunteer to present his or her solution and explain the reasoning for each step that was used. After the presentation, elicit comments or questions from other children. Then ask if anyone used a different way to solve the problem. Have that child present his or her work and follow up with another class discussion. Continue the presentations and discussions as both opportunity and time permit.

 Professional Development Videos

 **Interactive Student Edition**

Personal Math Trainer

Math on the Spot Video

iT iTools: Base-Ten Blocks

HMH Mega Math

Daily Routines

Common Core

 Problem of the Day 8.8

Fact Families Write three other facts using the same numbers:

6 + 8 = 14

$8 + 6 = 14$; $14 - 8 = 6$; $14 - 6 = 8$

Vocabulary

GO DIGITAL
• Interactive Student Edition
• Multimedia eGlossary

✚➖ Fluency Builder
✕➗

Common Core Fluency Standard 1.OA.C.6

Basic Facts Within 10

Materials Addition Fact Cards (see *eTeacher Resources*)

Have children work in groups of 4 or 5. Give each child a card. Tell one child in each group to show the card. Group members find the sum. The child with the card confirms the sum. Children continue until each child in the group has had a turn.

✚➖ Pages 86–87 in *Strategies and Practice for Skills and Facts*
✕➗ *Fluency* provide additional fluency support for this lesson.

Literature Connection

From the Grab-and-Go™ Differentiated Centers Kit

Children read the book and learn about 2-digit addition and subtraction with regrouping.

Party Plans

❶ ENGAGE

with the Interactive Student Edition

Essential Question
How can drawing a picture help you explain how to solve an addition problem?

Making Connections
Invite children to share what they know about adding tens and ones.

• **How can you draw a picture to show tens and ones? How can you use a model to show tens and ones?** Answers will vary.

Learning Activity
What is the problem the children are trying to solve? Connect the story to the problem. Direct children's attention to the ants.

• **How many ants are in the group to start?** 20 ants

• **How many ants join the group?** 4 ants

• **What question does Avery have?** She wants to know how many ants there are.

Literacy and Mathematics
Choose one or both of the following activities.

• Have small groups act out the story about the ants.

• Ask children to draw pictures showing what happens in the lesson opener. Then have children label their drawings with words, phrases, and numbers.

② EXPLORE

Unlock the Problem

Materials base-ten blocks, connecting cubes, Hundred Chart (see eTeacher Resources), MathBoard
Read the problem aloud as children listen.

Kelly gets 6 new toy cars. He already has 18 toy cars. How many does he have now?

Work through the Problem Solving graphic organizer together. Ask the following questions to guide children through the solution process.

- **How can you show how many toy cars Kelly already has?** Possible answer: I can use 18 connecting cubes.

- **How can you show how many new toy cars Kelly gets?** Possible answer: I can use 6 connecting cubes.

Have children draw quick pictures to show 18 and 6.

- **What is another way you could model the number of cars Kelly has?** Possible answer: I can use 1 tens block and 8 ones to show 18. I can use 6 ones to show 6.

Accept any reasonable explanations for how children solve the problem. Encourage discussion of as many different approaches as time allows. Drawings should match the reasoning children use.

MP1 Make sense of problems and persevere in solving them.

- **How does making a ten help in addition problems?** Possible answer: When I make a ten, one of the addends has 0 in the ones place and it is easier to see how many ones in all.

ELL Strategy:
Rephrase

Ask children to listen carefully and rephrase problems. Read the following problem.

- **Carter has 15 marbles. Chang has 17 marbles. How many marbles do they have in all?**

- **What do you need to find?** How many marbles altogether.

- **What information do you need?** Carter has 15 marbles and Chang has 17 marbles.

- **How can you solve this problem?** Possible answer: I make tens. 20 + 12 = 32. 15 + 17 = 32.

1.NBT.C.4 Add within 100, including adding a two-digit number and a one-digit number, and adding a two-digit number and a multiple of 10, using concrete models or drawings and strategies based on place value, properties of operations, and/ or the relationship between addition and subtraction; relate the strategy to a written method and explain the reasoning used. Understand that in adding two-digit numbers, one adds tens and tens, ones and ones; and sometimes it is necessary to compose a ten.

Progress to Algebra

Name _____

Problem Solving •
Addition Word Problems

**HANDS ON
Lesson 8.8**

Essential Question How can drawing a picture help you explain how to solve an addition problem?

Common Core **Number and Operations in Base Ten—1.NBT.C.4**
MATHEMATICAL PRACTICES
MP1, MP2, MP6, MP8

Kelly gets 6 new toy cars.
He already has 18 toy cars.
How many does he have now?

🔑 **Unlock the Problem**

What do I need to find?

how many ~toy cars~
Kelly has now

What information do I need to use?

Kelly has __18__ cars.

He gets __6__ more cars.

Show how to solve the problem.

Possible answer:

Problem Type:
Add To • Result Unknown

20 + 4 = 24 cars

18   6

I made a ten.

🏠 **HOME CONNECTION** • Being able to show and explain how to solve a problem helps your child build on their understanding of addition.

Chapter 8

four hundred seventy-nine **479**

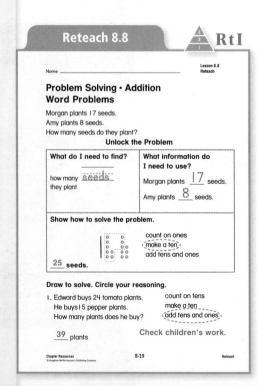

© Houghton Mifflin Harcourt Publishing Company • Image Credits: ©SketchMaster/Shutterstock

Try Another Problem

Draw and write to solve. Check children's drawings.
Explain your reasoning. Possible explanations shown.

- What do I need to find?
- What information do I need to use?

1. Aisha picks 60 blueberries to make a pie. Then she picks 12 more to eat. How many blueberries does Aisha pick?

72 blueberries

I counted on 6 tens from 12.

2. Yuri collects 21 cans for the school food drive. Leo collects 36 cans. How many cans do Yuri and Leo collect?

57 cans

I added tens and tens, then ones and ones.

Math Talk: Possible answer: 60 is the same as 6 tens, so I can start at 12 and count on 6 tens: 12, *22*, *32*, *42*, *52*, *62*, *72*. Aisha picks 72 blueberries.

480 four hundred eighty

Math Talk

MATHEMATICAL PRACTICES 6

Explain the addition strategy you used to solve Exercise 1.

© Houghton Mifflin Harcourt Publishing Company • Image Credits: (tc) ©PhotoDisc/Getty Images

---

③ EXPLAIN

Try Another Problem

MP4 Model with mathematics. Provide base-ten blocks, connecting cubes, and Hundred Charts for children to use if they need them. Use these questions to guide children through Exercise 1.

- **What do you need to find?** how many blueberries Aisha picked

- **What information do you need to use?** 60 blueberries, 12 more blueberries

- **How can you model the problem to find how many blueberries Aisha picked?** Possible answers: I can use connecting cubes to show the two groups and then find how many; I can use a hundred chart: first I can find 60 and then I can count on 1 ten and 2 ones; I can use base-ten blocks to show the two groups and then find how many.

 Math Talk **MP6 Attend to precision.** Use **Math Talk** to focus on children's understanding of using different addition strategies to solve problems.

- **Did you use the same strategy to solve Exercise 2?** Possible answer: No. **Why not?** Possible answer: Exercise 1 has a number that is only tens so it is easy to count on from that number; for exercise 2 I had to make a ten before I could count on by ten.

MP1 Make sense of problems and persevere in solving them.

- **What should you do if you try a strategy and it doesn't help you solve the problem?** Possible answer: Reread the problem and think of a different strategy to use.

 You may suggest that children place a completed Try Another Problem in their portfolios.

Advanced Learners

Visual / Kinesthetic
Small Group

Materials straws cut in half, buttons

- Give small groups 100 straws. Ask one child to make up an addition word problem, such as the following:

  Lilly made 24 muffins. Max made 36 muffins. How many muffins did Lilly and Max make? 60 muffins

- Another child models the two addends. To show tens, the child uses 1 straw to represent one ten. To show ones, the child uses buttons.

- Another child from the group writes an addition number sentence to find the sum.

- Have children take turns writing problems, modeling with straws and buttons, and writing addition number sentences.

 COMMON ERRORS

Error Children may record tens as ones.

Example For Exercise 1, children draw 6 ones to represent 60 blueberries.

Springboard to Learning Have children explain how many ones and tens are in the number 60. Then have children model the tens and ones using base-ten blocks.

Lesson 8.8   480

4 ELABORATE

Share and Show

MP4 Model with mathematics. Have children continue to use models to solve addition problems. Then have children use their MathBoards to draw quick pictures and explain the addition strategies they used.

Use the checked exercises for **Quick Check.**

✓ Quick Check ⟁ RtI

If ➤ a child misses the checked exercises

Then ➤ **Differentiate Instruction** with
- Reteach 8.8
- Personal Math Trainer 1.NBT.C.4
- RtI Tier 1 Activity (online)

THINK SMARTER

MP2 Reason abstractly and quantitatively.

Exercise 5 requires children to use higher order thinking skills. Children must recognize that to get across the yard and back, they must use 10 twice.

Math on the Spot Video Tutor

Use this video to help children model and solve this type of *Think Smarter* problem.

GO DIGITAL **Math on the Spot** videos are in the Interactive Student Edition and at *www.thinkcentral.com.*

Name _____

Share and Show

Check children's drawings and explanations.

MATHEMATICAL PRACTICE ② **Use Reasoning**
Draw and write to solve.

3. Tyra sees 48 geese in the field. Then she sees 17 more geese in the sky. How many geese does Tyra see?

___65___ geese

_____

4. Jade paints 35 circles and 45 triangles in art class. How many shapes does Jade paint?

___80___ shapes

_____

5. THINK SMARTER It takes 10 hops to get across the yard. How many hops does it take to get across the yard and back?

___20___ hops

Possible answer: I drew 1 ten for 10 hops across the yard and 1 ten for 10 hops back.

Chapter 8 • Lesson 8   four hundred eighty-one **481**

PROBLEM TYPE SITUATIONS

Addition and Subtraction

Add To • Result Unknown
Exercises: 1, 2, 3, 4, 6, 8

Put Together/Take Apart • Total Unknown
Exercises: 5, 7

Compare • Bigger Unknown
Exercise: 7

On Your Own

Choose a way to solve. Draw or write to explain.

6. **THINK SMARTER** Julian sells 3 books of tickets for the school fair. Each book has 20 tickets. How many tickets does Julian sell?

___60___ tickets

7. **GO DEEPER** I have some red roses and pink roses. I have 14 red roses. I have 8 more pink roses than red roses. How many roses do I have?

___36___ roses

8. **THINK SMARTER +** Ella sees 27 . She sees 28 . How many does Ella see? Circle the number that makes this sentence true.

 Personal Math Trainer

Ella sees
| 48 |
| 51 |
| (55) |
 in all.

 TAKE HOME ACTIVITY • Ask your child to solve 16 + 7, 30 + 68, and 53 + 24. Ask him or her to explain how they solved each problem.

482 four hundred eighty-two

 **DIFFERENTIATED INSTRUCTION** **INDEPENDENT ACTIVITIES**

Grab-and-Go!™
Differentiated Centers Kit

Activities
Regroup

Children complete orange Activity Card 20 by modeling addition of two-digit numbers with regrouping.

Literature
Party Plans

Children read the book and learn about 2-digit addition and subtraction with regrouping.

Games
Flying Along

Children practice 2-digit addition with regrouping.

On Your Own

MP1 Make sense of problems and persevere in solving them. If children answered Exercises 3 and 4 correctly, assign Exercises 6–8. Suggest children choose different strategies to complete the exercises.

GO DEEPER **Multi-Step**

Exercise 7 is a multi-step problem. One way to solve it is to determine the number of pink roses by adding 8 to 14. Then the number of pink roses is added to the number of red roses, 14, to find how many roses are in the garden.

THINK SMARTER +
Personal Math Trainer

Be sure to assign Exercise 8 to children in the Personal Math Trainer. It features an animation to help them model and answer the problem. Children interpret a word problem and apply what they have learned about using models to add two-digit numbers. Children who choose 48 may not have added the ones. Those who choose 51 may have found 15 ones and transposed the digits.

⑤ EVALUATE Formative Assessment

Essential Question

Reflect Using the Language Objective Have child pairs design a poster to answer the Essential Question.

How can drawing a picture help you explain how to solve an addition problem? Possible answer: It can help me see each part of the problem so I can find the sum.

Math Journal **WRITE** Math

Draw a picture to show how to find 12 + 37.

Practice and Homework

Use the Practice and Homework pages to provide children with more practice of the concepts and skills presented in this lesson. Children master their understanding as they complete practice items and then challenge their critical thinking skills with Problem Solving. Use the Write Math section to determine children's understanding of content for this lesson. Encourage children to use their Math Journals to record their answers.

Name _____

Problem Solving • Addition Word Problems

COMMON CORE STANDARD—1.NBT.C.4
Use place value understanding and properties of operations to add and subtract.

Draw and write to solve. Explain your reasoning.

Check children's work.

1. Jean has 10 fish. She gets 4 more fish. How many fish does she have now?

_____

— — — — — — — — — — — —

_____

__14__ fish

2. Courtney buys 2 bags of apples. Each bag has 20 apples. How many apples does she buy?

_____

— — — — — — — — — — — —

_____

__40__ apples

3. John bakes 18 blueberry muffins and 12 banana muffins for the bake sale. How many muffins does he bake?

_____

— — — — — — — — — — — —

_____

__30__ muffins

4.  Draw a picture to show how to find 12 + 37.

Check children's work.

© Houghton Mifflin Harcourt Publishing Company

Chapter 8

four hundred eighty-three **483**

Mathematical Practices in Your Classroom

CCSS.Math.Practice.MP3 Construct viable arguments and critique the reasoning of others.

Using viable arguments and communicating reasoning demonstrates a child's deeper understanding of mathematical concepts.

Finding an error in a solution and explaining how to correct it shows that a child has a solid understanding of the underlying mathematical concepts.

- After working through some correct examples, demonstrate an incorrect example of solving a problem. This will help children recognize and correct errors in their own work.
- As you walk through steps one at a time, discuss whether each step is performed correctly. This systematic process will give children time to identify the step in which the error occurred.

Help children recognize and correct errors in word problems.

- **Hannah brought 27 cat toys and 18 dog toys to sell at the fair. She says she has 35 toys to sell. Has Hannah made an error? Explain.** Yes. Hannah has more than 35 toys to sell.
- **You know Hannah made an error finding the sum of the toys. How did she make her error?** Possible answer: When Hannah made a ten from the 7 ones and 8 ones, she forgot to put it with the other tens.
- **What can Hannah do to check her work?** Possible answer: Hannah can use connecting cubes to model the addition; Hannah can draw a picture to check her addition.

1. Amy has 9 books about dogs.
   She has 13 books about cats.
   How many books does she
   have about dogs and cats?
   Solve. Show your work. Write the number.   __22__ books

2. What is the sum for $4 + 2 + 4$?
   Write the number.

   __10__

3. Solve. Use the ten frame to make a
   ten to help you subtract. Ray has
   14 pens. 8 are black. The rest
   are blue. How many pens are blue?   __6__ blue pens

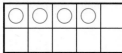

FOR MORE PRACTICE
GO TO THE
Personal Math Trainer

Continue concepts and skills practice with
Lesson Check. Use Spiral Review to engage
children in previously taught concepts and to
promote content retention. Common Core
standards are correlated to each section.

Related Addition and Subtraction

LESSON AT A GLANCE

FOCUS   COHERENCE   RIGOR

F C R Focus:

Common Core State Standards

1.NBT.C.4 Add within 100, including adding a two–digit number and a one–digit number, and adding a two–digit number and a multiple of 10, using concrete models or drawings and strategies based on place value, properties of operations, and/or the relationship between addition and subtraction; relate the strategy to a written method and explain the reasoning used. Understand that in adding two–digit numbers, one adds tens and tens, ones and ones; and sometimes it is necessary to compose a ten.

MATHEMATICAL PRACTICES (See *Mathematical Practices in GO Math!* in the *Planning Guide* for full text.) **MP2** Reason abstractly and quantitatively. **MP3** Construct viable arguments and critique the reasoning of others. **MP7** Look for and make use of structure.

F C R Coherence:

Standards Across the Grades
Before	Grade 1	After
K.NBT.A.1	1.NBT.C.4	2.NBT.B.5

F C R Rigor:

Level 1: Understand Concepts....................*Share and Show* (✓ Checked Items)
Level 2: Procedural Skills and Fluency.......*On Your Own, Practice and Homework*
Level 3: Applications................................*Think Smarter and Go Deeper*

Learning Objective
Use a hundred chart to find sums and differences.

Language Objective
Children demonstrate on a hundred chart and then explain the relationship between addition and subtraction.

Materials
MathBoard

F C R For more about how *GO Math!* fosters **Coherence** within the Content Standards and Mathematical Progressions for this chapter, see page 433J.

About the Math
Professional Development

Progress to Algebra
Teaching for Depth

In this lesson, children build their understanding of the relationship between addition and subtraction when working with two-digit numbers. Point out to children that subtraction undoes addition when working with two-digit numbers just as it does with addition and subtraction facts.

$5 + 3 = 8, 8 - 3 = 5$, so $51 + 30 = 81$ and $81 - 30 = 51$.

 Professional Development Videos

 GO DIGITAL

SE Interactive Student Edition

Personal Math Trainer

 Math on the Spot Video

*i*T *i*Tools: Number Charts

① ENGAGE
with the Interactive Student Edition

Essential Question
How can you use a hundred chart to show the relationship between addition and subtraction?

Making Connections
Ask children to tell what they know about using a hundred chart to add.

• **What direction do you move on a hundred chart when you want to add ones?** To the right **to add tens?** Down one row for each ten

• **What strategy are you using when you use a hundred chart?** Counting on

Learning Activity
What problem are children trying to solve? Connect the story to the problem. Ask the following questions.

• **How can you use a hundred chart to add 3 tens to a start number?** I can find the start number, then I can move down three rows to add three tens.

• **How can what you know about adding tens help you subtract tens using a hundred chart?** I know each row is one ten. I know that moving down one row adds one ten, so moving up one row takes away one ten.

Literacy and Mathematics
Choose from one or more of the following activities.

• Have children restate the problem and use the hundred chart to solve the problem.

• Model a number riddle such as, **I am thinking of a number that is 20 less than 40. What number am I thinking of?** Have children use a hundred chart to create similar riddles to share and solve.

② EXPLORE

Listen and Draw *Real World*

Read the following problem aloud.

Trevor collects 38 acorns. He collects 10 more acorns. How many acorns does Trevor have now?

Tell children they will use the hundred chart to solve the problem.

- **Start at 38. Count on 1 ten. Where do you stop?** 48 **How does using a hundred chart help you count up by tens?** Possible answer: As I move down a row, each row shows the number that is ten more.

Now read the next problem aloud.

Trevor has 48 acorns. He gives 10 acorns to his brother. How many acorns does Trevor have now?

- **Start at 48. Move up 1 row, or 1 ten. Where do you stop?** 38 **How can the hundred chart help you count back by tens?** Possible answer: As I move up one row, the number shown is ten less.

Math Talk **MP3 Construct viable arguments and critique the reasoning of others.** Use Math Talk to focus on children's understanding of how to use a hundred chart to add and subtract tens.

- **Why do you move in different directions on the chart to answer each question?** Possible answer: The way I move shows if I am adding or subtracting.

ELL Strategy:
Illustrate Understanding

Children illustrate their understanding of subtracting by multiples of 10.

Give children a hundred chart.

Write the problem **68 − 10 = ____** on the board.

Have children circle 68 on their charts and then move up one row to show subtracting 10.

- **What number is 10 less than 68? How did you find the answer?** 58

Continue with other subtraction problems involving multiples of 10.

Name _____

Related Addition and Subtraction

Lesson 8.9

Essential Question How can you use a hundred chart to show the relationship between addition and subtraction?

Common Core **Number and Operations in Base Ten—1.NBT.C.4**

MATHEMATICAL PRACTICES
MP2, MP3, MP7

Listen and Draw *Real World*

Use the hundred chart to solve the problems.

1	2	3	4	5	6	7	8	9	10
11	12	13	14	15	16	17	18	19	20
21	22	23	24	25	26	27	28	29	30
31	32	33	34	35	36	37	38	39	40
41	42	43	44	45	46	47	48	49	50
51	52	53	54	55	56	57	58	59	60
61	62	63	64	65	66	67	68	69	70
71	72	73	74	75	76	77	78	79	80
81	82	83	84	85	86	87	88	89	90
91	92	93	94	95	96	97	98	99	100

Math Talk: Possible answer: For Trevor, I put my finger on 38 and move down 1 row. I end on 48, so Trevor has 48 acorns now. Then I put my finger on 48 and move up 1 row to count back 1 ten. I end on 38, so Trevor has 38 acorns now.

Math Talk MATHEMATICAL PRACTICES ③

Apply Describe how you can use a hundred chart to find the sum and the difference.

FOR THE TEACHER • Read the following problems. Trevor collects 38 acorns. He collects 10 more acorns. How many acorns does Trevor have now? Trevor has 48 acorns. He gives 10 acorns to his brother. How many acorns does Trevor have now?

Chapter 8

Problem Type:
Add To • Result Unknown

Problem Type:
Take From • Result Unknown

four hundred eighty-five **485**

Reteach 8.9 ▲ RtI

Name _____

Lesson 8.9
Reteach

Related Addition and Subtraction
You can count on and back by tens to add and subtract.

1	2	3	4	5	6	7	8	9	10
11	12	13	14	15	16	17	18	19	20
21	22	23	24	25	26	27	28	29	30
31	32	33	34	35	36	37	38	39	40
41	42	43	44	45	46	47	48	49	50
51	52	53	54	55	56	57	58	59	60
61	62	63	64	65	66	67	68	69	70
71	72	73	74	75	76	77	78	79	80
81	82	83	84	85	86	87	88	89	90
91	92	93	94	95	96	97	98	99	100

Start at 68. Move down to count on by 3 tens. Count
78, 88, 98
68 + 30 = 98

Start at 98. Move up to count back by 3 tens. Count
88, 78, 68
98 − 30 = 68

Use the hundred chart to add and subtract. Count on and back by tens.

1. 42 + 20 = 62

62 − 20 = 42

2. 24 + 60 = 84

84 − 60 = 24

Chapter Resources
© Houghton Mifflin Harcourt Publishing Company

8-21

Reteach

Enrich 8.9 **Differentiated Instruction**

Name _____

Lesson 8.9
Enrich

Ticket Counter

Use the hundred chart to solve. Circle the number of tickets Max has left after the petting zoo.

Max has 90 tickets to use at the fair.

First, Max uses 40 tickets to buy lemonade.

Then Max uses 5 tickets to get into the petting zoo.

1	2	3	4	5	6	7	8	9	10
11	12	13	14	15	16	17	18	19	20
21	22	23	24	25	26	27	28	29	30
31	32	33	34	35	36	37	38	39	40
41	42	43	44	45	46	47	48	49	50
51	52	53	54	55	56	57	58	59	60
61	62	63	64	65	66	67	68	69	70
71	72	73	74	75	76	77	78	79	80
81	82	83	84	85	86	87	88	89	90
91	92	93	94	95	96	97	98	99	100

Writing and Reasoning Write two number sentences to show how Max used his tickets. Explain.

90 − 40 = 50 and 50 − 5 = 45; Possible answer: Max has 90 tickets. Subtract the 40 tickets he uses for lemonade. He has 50 tickets left. Then subtract 5 from 50 for the tickets he uses for the petting zoo. Max has 45 tickets left.

Chapter Resources
© Houghton Mifflin Harcourt Publishing Company

8-22

Enrich

1.NBT.C.4 Add within 100, including adding a two-digit number and a one-digit number, and adding a two-digit number and a multiple of 10, using concrete models or drawings and strategies based on place value, properties of operations, and/ or the relationship between addition and subtraction; relate the strategy to a written method and explain the reasoning used. Understand that in adding two-digit numbers, one adds tens and tens, ones and ones; and sometimes it is necessary to compose a ten.

Progress to Algebra

Model and Draw

You can use a hundred chart to find a sum and a difference.

Start at **29**. Count on four tens.
39, 49, 59, 69

$29 + 40 = \underline{69}$

Start at **69**. Count back four tens.
59, 49, 39, 29

$69 - 40 = \underline{29}$

1	2	3	4	5	6	7	8	9	10
11	12	13	14	15	16	17	18	19	20
21	22	23	24	25	26	27	28	29	30
31	32	33	34	35	36	37	38	39	40
41	42	43	44	45	46	47	48	49	50
51	52	53	54	55	56	57	58	59	60
61	62	63	64	65	66	67	68	69	70
71	72	73	74	75	76	77	78	79	80
81	82	83	84	85	86	87	88	89	90
91	92	93	94	95	96	97	98	99	100

Share and Show MATH BOARD

Use the hundred chart to add and subtract.
Count on and back by tens.

1. $56 + 20 = \underline{76}$

$76 - 20 = \underline{56}$

2. $48 + 50 = \underline{98}$

$98 - 50 = \underline{48}$

486 four hundred eighty-six

© Houghton Mifflin Harcourt Publishing Company

Advanced Learners
Visual / Verbal
Small Group / Partners

Materials Hundred Chart (see *eTeacher Resources*)

- Write $56 - 30 - 2 = \underline{}$ on the board. Have partners use a Hundred Chart to solve. What is the difference? 24

- Have partners take turns creating and solving subtraction sentences where they first count back by tens, then count back by ones. **What patterns do you notice?**

- Repeat the activity with addition sentences where the children first add ones, and then add tens.

---

③ EXPLAIN

Model and Draw Common Core MATHEMATICAL PRACTICES

MP7 Look for and make use of structure. Work through the model with children to solve 29 + 40. Have children trace the sum.

- **If you move down from 29 to 69 on the hundred chart, how many tens have you added to 29?** 4 tens, or 40

Work through the model with children to solve 69 − 40. Have children trace the difference.

- **If you move up from 69 to 29 on the hundred chart, how many tens have you subtracted from 69?** 4 tens, or 40

Share and Show MATH BOARD

Have children use the hundred chart to complete Exercises 1 and 2. Read each exercise and have children tell whether they will count up or back by tens.

- **How could you use the hundred chart to subtract 50 from 98?** Start at 98. Move up 5 rows to 48.

- **How do you know your answer is correct?** Possible answer: I know 50 has 5 tens. I know I have to move up 5 rows. When I move up 5 rows, I am on 48 so my answer is correct.

Use the checked exercises for **Quick Check.**

 Quick Check

If a child misses the checked exercises

Then **Differentiate Instruction** with
- Reteach 8.9
- Personal Math Trainer 1.NBT.C.4
- RtI Tier 1 Activity (online)

⚠ COMMON ERRORS

Error Children may count on instead of counting back.

Example In Exercise 1, children write a difference of 96.

Springboard to Learning Have children recall that they move down by tens to add. To subtract, children need to move up by tens.

4 ELABORATE

On Your Own

MP7 Look for and make use of structure.
If children answered Exercises 1 and 2 correctly, assign Exercises 3–7. Work through the model with children to find the sum and the difference, reinforcing the use of a hundred chart to find both.

 THINK SMARTER

Exercise 7 requires children to use higher order thinking skills as they apply what they have learned to solve a two-step word problem.

**Math on the Spot
Video Tutor**
Use this video to help children model and solve this type of *Think Smarter* problem.

GO DIGITAL Math on the Spot videos are in the Interactive Student Edition and at *www.thinkcentral.com*.

 GO DEEPER

MP1 Make sense of problems and persevere in solving them. To extend thinking, challenge children to solve problems that are not related. Then have children write the related addition or subtraction fact for each problem. Have volunteers share their solutions.

$88 + 10 = \underline{98}$
$43 + 40 = \underline{83}$
$29 - 10 = \underline{19}$
$67 - 30 = \underline{37}$

**MP2 Reason abstractly and quantitatively.
Look at the related addition facts. How can you use the numbers in the addition facts to write related subtraction facts?** Possible answer: I can take the sum, then subtract one addend to find the answer, which will be the other addend. For example: 98 – 10 = 88.

In Grade 1, children learn to compute differences of two-digit numbers. Differences of multiples of 10, such as 70 – 20, can be viewed as 7 tens minus 2 tens and represented with concrete models. Children use the relationship between subtraction and addition when they view 70 – 20 as an unknown addend addition problem, 20 + ____ = 70, and know that 5 tens must be added to 20 to make 70, so 70 – 20 = 50.

Name _____

On Your Own

1	2	3	4	5	6	7	8	9	10
11	12	13	14	15	16	17	18	19	20
21	22	23	24	25	26	27	28	29	30
31	32	33	34	35	36	37	38	39	40
41	42	43	44	45	46	47	48	49	50
51	52	53	54	55	56	57	58	59	60
61	62	63	64	65	66	67	68	69	70
71	72	73	74	75	76	77	78	79	80
81	82	83	84	85	86	87	88	89	90
91	92	93	94	95	96	97	98	99	100

How can you use the hundred chart to find the sum and the difference?

$28 + 60 = \underline{88}$

$88 - 60 = \underline{28}$

MATHEMATICAL PRACTICE ⑦ Look for a Pattern Use the hundred chart to add and subtract. Count on and back by tens.

3. $36 + 30 = \underline{66}$

$66 - 30 = \underline{36}$

4. $73 + 10 = \underline{83}$

$83 - 10 = \underline{73}$

5. $25 + 70 = \underline{95}$

$95 - 70 = \underline{25}$

6. $18 + 40 = \underline{58}$

$58 - 40 = \underline{18}$

7. **THINK SMARTER** Solve.
There are 73 bees in a hive. 10 bees fly away. Then 10 more bees fly into the hive. How many bees are in the hive now?

$\underline{73}$ bees

© Houghton Mifflin Harcourt Publishing Company

PROBLEM TYPE SITUATIONS

Addition and Subtraction

Add To • Result Unknown
Exercises: 7, 9

Take From • Result Unknown
Exercises: 7, 8, 9

Problem Solving • Applications (Real World)   WRITE Math

Solve. Draw or write to show your work.

8. **THINK SMARTER** There are 38 ants on a rock. 10 move to the grass. 10 walk up a tree. How many ants are on the rock now?

_18_ ants

9. **GO DEEPER** There are 27 birds at the park. 50 more birds come. Then 50 fly away. How many birds are at the park now?

_27_ birds

10. **THINK SMARTER** Match the math sentences that count on and back by tens.

$25 + 40 = ?$ $65 + 20 = ?$ $45 + 30 = ?$

$65 - 40 = ?$ $75 - 30 = ?$ $85 - 20 = ?$

 TAKE HOME ACTIVITY • On slips of paper, write 36 + 40 and 76 − 40. Ask your child to explain how to use the hundred chart to count on and back by tens to find the sum and the difference.

488 four hundred eighty-eight

Problem Solving • Applications (Real World)

MP7 Look for and make use of structure. Have children solve each problem. Children may need to use a hundred chart.

THINK SMARTER

In Exercise 8, children use higher order thinking skills to solve a two-step problem. First they must subtract the number of ants that move to the grass. Then they must subtract that same number of ants that walk up a tree. Children must recognize that they are subtracting the same number two times to solve the problem.

GO DEEPER **Multi-Step**

In Exercise 9, children use higher order thinking skills to solve a two-step problem that involves adding and then subtracting the same number. Ask children to explain why, at the end of the story, they have the same number of birds that they had at the beginning of the story.

THINK SMARTER

Exercise 10 assesses whether children know how to use related facts to solve addition and subtraction problems using two-digit numbers. Some children who answer incorrectly may understand only single-digit related facts. Children should be able to use mental math to match the addition and subtraction expressions, but a hundred chart may help any who struggle.

5 EVALUATE   Formative Assessment

Essential Question

Reflect Using the Language Objective Have children demonstrate on a hundred chart and then explain to answer the Essential Question.

How can you use a hundred chart to show the relationship between addition and subtraction? I count on and back the same numbers because both problems use the same numbers.

Math Journal   WRITE Math

Write a number sentence to subtract 3 tens from 93.

 DIFFERENTIATED INSTRUCTION **INDEPENDENT ACTIVITIES**

Differentiated Centers Kit

Activities
Count On

 Children complete blue Activity Card 20 by counting on to add two-digit numbers.

Games
Basic Facts Race

 Children find missing numbers in addition and subtraction sentences.

Practice and Homework

Use the Practice and Homework pages to provide children with more practice of the concepts and skills presented in this lesson. Children master their understanding as they complete practice items and then challenge their critical thinking skills with Problem Solving. Use the Write Math section to determine children's understanding of content for this lesson. Encourage children to use their Math Journals to record their answers.

Related Addition and Subtraction

Common Core   COMMON CORE STANDARDS—1.NBT.C.4
Use place value understanding and properties of operations to add and subtract.

Use the hundred chart to add and subtract. Count on and back by tens.

1. $16 + 60 =$ __76__

   $76 - 60 =$ __16__

2. $61 + 30 =$ __91__

   $91 - 30 =$ __61__

3. $64 + 20 =$ __84__

   $84 - 20 =$ __64__

1	2	3	4	5	6	7	8	9	10
11	12	13	14	15	16	17	18	19	20
21	22	23	24	25	26	27	28	29	30
31	32	33	34	35	36	37	38	39	40
41	42	43	44	45	46	47	48	49	50
51	52	53	54	55	56	57	58	59	60
61	62	63	64	65	66	67	68	69	70
71	72	73	74	75	76	77	78	79	80
81	82	83	84	85	86	87	88	89	90
91	92	93	94	95	96	97	98	99	100

Problem Solving (Real World)

Choose a way to solve. Draw or write to show your work.

4. There are 53 leaves in a tree. 20 leaves blow away. How many leaves are left in the tree?

   __33__ leaves

5. **WRITE** Math Write a number sentence to subtract 3 tens from 93.

   Check children's work.
   _____

© Houghton Mifflin Harcourt Publishing Company

I. What is 78 − 20?
Write the number.

<u>58</u>

1	2	3	4	5	6	7	8	9	10
11	12	13	14	15	16	17	18	19	20
21	22	23	24	25	26	27	28	29	30
31	32	33	34	35	36	37	38	39	40
41	42	43	44	45	46	47	48	49	50
51	52	53	54	55	56	57	58	59	60
61	62	63	64	65	66	67	68	69	70
71	72	73	74	75	76	77	78	79	80
81	82	83	84	85	86	87	88	89	90
91	92	93	94	95	96	97	98	99	100

2. What is 37 + 50?
Write the number.

<u>87</u>

3. Use the model.
What is the difference of 7 − 3?
Write the number.

$$7 - 3 = \underline{4}$$

4. What is the sum for 0 + 7?
Write the number.

<u>7</u>

FOR MORE PRACTICE
GO TO THE
Personal Math Trainer

Continue concepts and skills practice with Lesson Check. Use Spiral Review to engage children in previously taught concepts and to promote content retention. Common Core standards are correlated to each section.

Practice Addition and Subtraction

LESSON AT A GLANCE

F C R Focus:

Common Core State Standards

▪ **1.NBT.C.4** Add within 100, including adding a two-digit number and a one-digit number, and adding a two-digit number and a multiple of 10, using concrete models or drawings and strategies based on place value, properties of operations, and/or the relationship between addition and subtraction; relate the strategy to a written method and explain the reasoning used. Understand that in adding two-digit numbers, one adds tens and tens, ones and ones; and sometimes it is necessary to compose a ten.

▪ **1.NBT.C.6** Subtract multiples of 10 in the range 10-90 from multiples of 10 in the range 10-90 (positive or zero differences), using concrete models or drawings and strategies based on place value, properties of operations, and/or the relationship between addition and subtraction; relate the strategy to a written method and explain the reasoning used.

MATHEMATICAL PRACTICES (See *Mathematical Practices in GO Math!* in the *Planning Guide* for full text.)
MP1 Make sense of problems and persevere in solving them. **MP2** Reason abstractly and quantitatively.
MP3 Construct viable arguments and critique the reasoning of others. **MP8** Look for and express regularity in repeated reasoning.

F C R Coherence:

Standards Across the Grades
Before   **Grade 1**   **After**
K.NBT.A.1 1.NBT.C.4 2.NBT.B.5
          1.NBT.C.6

F C R Rigor:

Level 1: Understand Concepts....................*Share and Show* (✓ Checked Items)
Level 2: Procedural Skills and Fluency.......*On Your Own, Practice and Homework*
Level 3: Applications..................................*Think Smarter and Go Deeper*

Learning Objective

Add and subtract within 100, including continued practice with facts within 20.

Language Objective

Child teams discuss and share the different ways you can use to add and subtract.

Materials

MathBoard, base-ten blocks, connecting cubes, Hundred Chart (see *eTeacher Resources*)

F C R For more about how *GO Math!* fosters **Coherence** within the Content Standards and Mathematical Progressions for this chapter, see page 433J.

About the Math

Professional Development

Progress to Algebra
Why Teach This

Teachers may think that knowing several ways of doing the same thing confuses children. Rather than confusing children, learning a variety of approaches empowers them. Since children have many different modalities, teaching a variety of strategies and showing different models for concepts and operations helps all children find a way that works for them. It also gives children alternative methods of problem solving when they are having trouble finding a solution.

 Professional Development Videos

GO DIGITAL

 **Interactive Student Edition**

 **Personal Math Trainer**

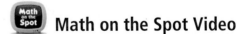 **Math on the Spot Video**

 **Animated Math Models**

iT *iTools:* Base-Ten Blocks

 HMH Mega Math

Daily Routines
Common Core

 Problem of the Day 8.10

Basic Facts Which is true? Circle your answer. Which is false? Cross out your answer.

$$\boxed{11 - 5 = 6 - 0} \qquad \cancel{2 + 7 = 12 - 7}$$

Have children give other examples of expressions that are true and false.

Vocabulary

GO DIGITAL
- Interactive Student Edition
- Multimedia eGlossary

 **Fluency Builder**
Make It, Say It, Solve It

Common Core Fluency Standard 1.OA.C.6

Materials: Number cards: 0–20, plus sign, minus sign (optional), hundred chart (See *eTeacher Resources*)

Have children work in pairs. Give each pair of children a set of number cards. Have children place the cards face down.

Have one partner draw two cards and place them face up. Have the other partner place the plus sign between the two numbers to make a number fact, and then say the number fact aloud. Have the partner who drew the number cards say the answer for the addition fact. Have children use the hundred charts and strategies they know to check the answer.

Repeat the activity by having children change roles.

Extend the activity by having children use the minus sign instead of the plus sign. Help children understand the larger number will always be the first number when they use the minus sign.

Pages 86–87 in *Strategies and Practice for Skills and Facts Fluency* provide additional fluency support for this lesson.

① ENGAGE

with the Interactive Student Edition

Essential Question
What different ways can you use to add and subtract?

Making Connections
Help children recall strategies they have used to add and subtract.

- **What strategy would you use to solve 19 + 6?** Make a ten
- **What strategy would you use to solve 31 − 2?** Count back

Continue with other examples that illustrate strategies like counting on, doubles, doubles plus one, doubles minus one.

Learning Activity
What problem are children trying to solve? Connect the story to the problem. Ask the following questions.

- **What do you do first when you solve a problem?** Identify what I need to know.

- **How does using a strategy help you solve the problem?** Possible answers: A strategy helps me think about the numbers in a useful way.

- **Which strategy did you use?** Answers will vary. **Why?** Answers will vary.

Literacy and Mathematics
Choose from one or more of the following activities.

- Create a new problem using the same characters. Have children solve the problem and explain which strategy they used.

- Show a number fact and have a child quickly name a strategy they would use to solve that number fact. Have the class use that strategy to find the answer.

② **EXPLORE**

Listen and Draw

Materials base-ten blocks, connecting cubes, Hundred Chart
(see *eTeacher Resources*)

Read the following problem aloud as children listen attentively.

The class collects paper bags for an art project. Ron brings 7 more bags than Ben. Ben brings 35 bags. How many bags does Ron bring?

Provide the materials for children to use if they need to. Have children solve the problem using a strategy they choose.

- **How did you model the problem?** Possible answer: I used 3 tens and 5 ones to model 35 and 7 ones to model 7. I used 10 ones to make a ten. Then I counted the tens and ones. I have 4 tens and 2 ones, 42.

- **How does your drawing show the addition?** Possible answer: I drew 3 lines to show 3 tens and 5 circles to show 5 ones in 35. Then I drew 7 circles to show 7 ones. I circled 10 ones to make a ten. So my drawing shows 4 tens and 2 ones.

 MP1 Make sense of problems and persevere in solving them. Use Math Talk to focus on children's understanding of using different strategies to add and subtract.

- **Why show 7 as 5 + 2?** Possible answer: I already have 5 ones in 35 and I need 5 more to make a ten. It is easier to see the doubles fact 5 + 5 when I show 7 as 5 + 2.

 Strategy:
Cooperative Grouping

Have English Language Learners work in groups with native English speakers to solve addition and subtraction problems.

Write **34 + 7 = ____**.

Have children work together to solve the problem. Encourage children to tell how they solved the problem.

Listen as children work together and provide support as needed.

Repeat with a variety of addition and subtraction problems.

MP8 Look for and express regularity in repeated reasoning.

- **Why was it a good strategy to make a ten to help you solve this problem?** Possible answer: Once I made the ten, I could count the tens and count the ones more easily to find my answer.

1.NBT.C.4 Add within 100, including adding a two-digit number and a one-digit number, and adding a two-digit number and a multiple of 10, using concrete models or drawings and strategies based on place value, properties of operations, and/or the relationship between addition and subtraction; relate the strategy to a written method and explain the reasoning used. Understand that in adding two-digit numbers, one adds tens and tens, ones and ones; and sometimes it is necessary to compose a ten. **1.NBT.C.6** Subtract multiples of 10 in the range 10-90 from multiples of 10 in the range 10-90 (positive or zero differences), using concrete models or drawings and strategies based on place value, properties of operations, and/or the relationship between addition and subtraction; relate the strategy to a written method and explain the reasoning used.

Progress to Algebra →

Name _____

Lesson 8.10

Practice Addition and Subtraction
Essential Question What different ways can you use to add and subtract?

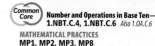 **Common Core** Number and Operations in Base Ten—
1.NBT.C.4, 1.NBT.C.6 *Also 1.OA.C.6*
MATHEMATICAL PRACTICES
MP1, MP2, MP3, MP8

Listen and Draw

Draw to show the problem.
Then solve.

Possible answer:

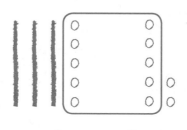

$$35 \; \oplus \; 7 \; \ominus \; 42$$

Math Talk: Possible answer: I need to add 7 to 35 to find how many paper bags Ron brings. 7 is the same as 5 + 2. First I added 5 to 35 to make 40, then 2 more is 42.

Problem Type:
Compare • Bigger Unknown
FOR THE TEACHER • Read the following problem. The class collects paper bags for an art project. Ron brings 7 more bags than Ben. Ben brings 35 bags. How many bags does Ron bring?

Math Talk MATHEMATICAL PRACTICES
Describe How did you solve the problem?

© Houghton Mifflin Harcourt Publishing Company

Chapter 8

four hundred ninety-one **491**

Reateach 8.10 ▲ **RtI**

Name _____ Lesson 8.10 Reteach

Practice Addition and Subtraction

You can use models to add and subtract.
13 + 5 = _18_
90 − 60 = _30_

Add or subtract.

1. 33 + 6 = _39_	2. 10 + 10 = _20_	3. 15 − 8 = _7_
4. 6 + 7 = _13_	5. 54 + 23 = _77_	6. 71 + 8 = _79_
7. 5 + 5 = _10_	8. 8 − 8 = _0_	9. 16 + 3 = _19_
10. 55 + 12 = _67_	11. 9 − 7 = _2_	12. 30 − 10 = _20_

Chapter Resources
© Houghton Mifflin Harcourt Publishing Company
8-23 Reteach

Enrich 8.10 ◄ **Differentiated Instruction**

Name _____ Lesson 8.10 Enrich

Use the Clue

Use the clue to write the number you add or subtract. Then solve.

1. The second number is 10 less than the first number.	38 − _28_ = _10_
2. The second number has 5 more ones than the first number.	22 + _27_ = _49_
3. The second number has 3 tens and 4 ones.	9 + _34_ = _43_
4. The second number has 0 tens and 0 ones.	55 + _0_ = _55_

 Writing and Reasoning Write a clue for an addend in the number sentence 15 + 25 = 40.

Possible answer: The second addend has 2 tens and 5 ones.

Chapter Resources
© Houghton Mifflin Harcourt Publishing Company
8-24 Enrich

Model and Draw

What ways have you learned to add and subtract?

$5 + 9 = \underline{14}$

THINK
$9 + 5$ is the same as $10 + \underline{?}$.

$50 - 30 = \underline{20}$

THINK
5 tens − 3 tens.

$51 + 21 = \underline{72}$

THINK
5 tens + 2 tens.
1 one + 1 one.

Share and Show MATH BOARD

Add or subtract.

1. $30 + 60 = \underline{90}$ 2. $73 + 5 = \underline{78}$ 3. $10 - 4 = \underline{6}$

4. $29 + 4 = \underline{33}$ 5. $9 + 9 = \underline{18}$ 6. $5 + 6 = \underline{11}$

7. $25 + 54 = \underline{79}$ 8. $15 - 8 = \underline{7}$ 9. $40 + 10 = \underline{50}$

10. $40 - 10 = \underline{30}$ 11. $14 - 7 = \underline{7}$ 12. $90 - 70 = \underline{20}$

13. $86 + 12 = \underline{98}$ 14. $1 + 9 = \underline{10}$ 15. $6 + 7 = \underline{13}$

16. $9 - 2 = \underline{7}$ 17. $8 + 31 = \underline{39}$ 18. $50 + 11 = \underline{61}$

492 four hundred ninety-two

---

③ EXPLAIN

Model and Draw Common Core MATHEMATICAL PRACTICES

MP1 Make sense of problems and persevere in solving them. Work through the models with children. Have children find the sum or difference for each model and discuss the strategies used.

- **What way can you use to find 5 + 9?**
  Possible answer: I can make a ten.
- **What way can you use to find 50 − 30?**
  Possible answer: I can subtract tens.
- **What way can you use to find 51 + 21?**
  Possible answer: I can add tens to tens and ones to ones.
- **How are these ways alike?** Possible answer: They all use tens.

Share and Show MATH BOARD

Have children complete the exercises by using a strategy of their own choosing.

- **How do you know your answer is correct?**
  I used a strategy that made sense with the problem, then I used my MathBoard to check my answer.

Use the checked exercises for **Quick Check**.

✓ **Quick Check** RtI

If → a child misses the checked exercises

Then → **Differentiate Instruction** with
- Reteach 8.10
- Personal Math Trainer 1.NBT.C.4, 1.NBT.C.6
- RtI Tier 1 Activity (online)

⚠ COMMON ERRORS

Error When adding two-digit and one-digit numbers, children may add the one-digit number as a ten.

Example In Exercise 4, children add $29 + 40$ and write 69 as the sum.

Springboard to Learning To help children understand their error, have them draw quick pictures to show each number. Then have them count the ones and tens to find the sum.

4 ELABORATE

On Your Own

MP8 Look for and express regularity in repeated reasoning. If children answered Exercises 17 and 18 correctly, assign Exercises 19–35.

MP8 Look for and express regularity in repeated reasoning. To extend thinking, have children generalize about what kinds of addition and subtraction problems might be appropriate to use with each strategy. Have children identify problems, such as Exercise 19, in which they used basic facts to solve. Have children identify problems, such as Exercises 24 and 31, in which they make a ten both as an addition strategy and as a subtraction strategy. Continue in this way with the strategies add or subtract tens, and add tens to tens and ones to ones.

- **Why don't you use the same strategy to solve all problems?** Possible answer: I have to pick a strategy that works for the problem I want to solve. For example, some problems I can solve just knowing basic facts and some problems I can solve more quickly by using the make a ten strategy. I pick a strategy based on the numbers I am working with.

THINK SMARTER

Exercise 35 requires children to use higher order thinking skills as they select a strategy to determine the number of stamps Lara collects.

Additional Example
Compare • Bigger Unknown

- **Makenna has 3 more apples than Taylor. Taylor has 5 apples. How many apples does Makenna have?** 8

Name _____

On Your Own

MATHEMATICAL PRACTICE 8 Use Repeated Reasoning Add or subtract.

19. $\begin{array}{r}12\\-\ 3\\\hline 9\end{array}$	20. $\begin{array}{r}10\\+10\\\hline 20\end{array}$	21. $\begin{array}{r}7\\+42\\\hline 49\end{array}$	22. $\begin{array}{r}41\\+36\\\hline 77\end{array}$
23. $\begin{array}{r}8\\+10\\\hline 18\end{array}$	24. $\begin{array}{r}16\\+\ 7\\\hline 23\end{array}$	25. $\begin{array}{r}6\\-6\\\hline 0\end{array}$	26. $\begin{array}{r}3\\+8\\\hline 11\end{array}$
27. $\begin{array}{r}64\\+\ 3\\\hline 67\end{array}$	28. $\begin{array}{r}60\\-30\\\hline 30\end{array}$	29. $\begin{array}{r}2\\+7\\\hline 9\end{array}$	30. $\begin{array}{r}5\\-1\\\hline 4\end{array}$
31. $\begin{array}{r}13\\-\ 5\\\hline 8\end{array}$	32. $\begin{array}{r}52\\+40\\\hline 92\end{array}$	33. $\begin{array}{r}3\\+2\\\hline 5\end{array}$	34. $\begin{array}{r}30\\+50\\\hline 80\end{array}$

Solve. Write or draw to explain.

35. **THINK SMARTER** Lara collects 8 more stamps than Samson. Samson collects 39 stamps. How many stamps does Lara collect?

___47___ stamps

PROBLEM TYPE SITUATIONS

Addition and Subtraction

Add To • Start Unknown
Exercise: 36

Compare • Bigger Unknown
Exercises: 35, 37

Problem Solving • Applications WRITE Math

Solve. Write or draw to explain.

Check children's work.

36. THINK SMARTER Jane drew some stars. Then she drew 9 more stars. Now there are 19 stars. How many stars did Jane draw first?

___10___ stars

37. THINK SMARTER Adel drew 10 more stars than Charlie. Charlie drew 24 stars. How many stars did Adel draw?

___34___ stars

38. GO DEEPER Write three ways to get a sum of 49.

Answers will vary.
Possible answer shown.

___40___ (+) ___9___ = 49

___24___ (+) ___25___ = 49

___1___ (+) ___48___ = 49

39. THINK SMARTER Find the sum of 23 and 30. Use any way to add.

$$23 + 30 = \underline{53}$$

Explain how you solved the problem.

> Check children's answers. Possible answer:
> I counted on 3 tens from 23.

 TAKE HOME ACTIVITY • Have your child explain how he or she solved Exercise 36.

494 four hundred ninety-four

© Houghton Mifflin Harcourt Publishing Company

DIFFERENTIATED INSTRUction INDEPENDENT ACTIVITIES

Differentiated Centers Kit

Activities
Neat Trick

Children complete purple Activity Card 20 by using place value and basic facts to add two-digit numbers.

Literature
Party Plans

Children read the book and learn about 2-digit addition and subtraction with regrouping.

Games
Flying Along

Children practice 2-digit addition with regrouping.

Problem Solving • Applications

Common Core MATHEMATICAL PRACTICES

THINK SMARTER

MP1 Make sense of problems and persevere in solving them. Have children read Exercises 36 and 37. Ask them how they will solve the problems. Have base-ten blocks and connecting cubes available for use if needed.

 Math on the Spot Video Tutor
Use this video to help children model and solve this type of *Think Smarter* problem.

 Math on the Spot videos are in the Interactive Student Edition and at *www.thinkcentral.com*.

GO DEEPER

MP2 Reason abstractly and quantitatively. Exercise 38 requires children to use higher order thinking skills as they work from a whole to write its different parts.

THINK SMARTER

Exercise 39 assesses whether children can use different strategies to help them add or subtract. Children who answer incorrectly may have added 3 rather than 30 (sum 26) or they may have added only the tens (sum 50). Remind children of strategies they can use or drawings that may help. Check explanations for an understanding of making a ten, adding tens, or adding tens and ones.

5 EVALUATE Formative Assessment

Essential Question

Reflect Using the Language Objective Have child teams discuss and share to answer the Essential Question.

What different ways can you use to add and subtract? Possible answer: I can make a ten; I can use basic facts; I can add or subtract tens; I can add tens to tens and ones to ones.

Math Journal  Math

Write two ways you could use to find 5 + 8.

Practice and Homework

Use the Practice and Homework pages to provide children with more practice of the concepts and skills presented in this lesson. Children master their understanding as they complete practice items and then challenge their critical thinking skills with Problem Solving. Use the Write Math section to determine children's understanding of content for this lesson. Encourage children to use their Math Journals to record their answers.

Practice Addition and Subtraction

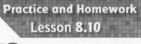

COMMON CORE STANDARDS—1.NBT.C.4, 1.NBT.C.6 *Use place value understanding and properties of operations to add and subtract.*

Add or subtract.

1.	2.	3.	4.	5.
20 + 20 **40**	90 − 30 **60**	52 + 4 **56**	62 + 21 **83**	39 − 10 **29**

6.	7.	8.	9.	10.
8 + 2 **10**	47 + 34 **81**	4 − 0 **4**	49 − 6 **43**	64 + 30 **94**

Problem Solving *Real World*

Solve. Write or draw to explain.   Check children's work.

11. Andrew read 17 pages of his book before dinner. He read 9 more pages after dinner. How many pages did he read?

$17 + 9 = 26$ **26** pages

12. **WRITE** *Math* Write two ways you could use to find $5 + 8$.

Check children's work.
_____
_____
_____

© Houghton Mifflin Harcourt Publishing Company

Lesson Check (1.NBT.C.4, 1.NBT.C.6)

1. What is the sum of 20 + 18?
   Write the sum.

   20 + 18 = __38__

2. What is the difference of 90 − 50?
   Write the difference.

   90 − 50 = __40__

Spiral Review (1.OA.A.1, 1.OA.C.6)

3. Use the model. What number
   sentence does this model show?
   Write the number sentence that
   the model shows.

   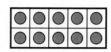

   __10__ + __3__ = __13__

4. Solve. Mo had some toys. He gave 6 away.
   Now he has 6 toys. How many toys did
   Mo start with?

   __12__ toys

FOR MORE PRACTICE
GO TO THE
Personal Math Trainer

Continue concepts and skills practice with Lesson Check. Use Spiral Review to engage children in previously taught concepts and to promote content retention. Common Core standards are correlated to each section.

Monitoring Common Core Success

Maintaining Focus on the Major Work

In Grade 1, part of the major work includes using place-value understanding and properties of operations to add and subtract (1.NBT.C). The focus of lessons 8.4–8.7 is to add a two-digit number with a one-digit number using place value and models to compose a ten if needed. In Lessons 8.8–8.9, children are introduced to problem solving strategies that involve the use of place value, properties of operations, and the relationship between addition and subtraction. A hundred chart and place-value table are presented as methods to solve addition and subtraction problems of base ten quantities.

Connecting Content Across Domains and Clusters

Throughout Lessons 8.4–8.10, children work within Cluster 1.NBT.C. In Lesson 8.4, children work with a hundred chart to add. This work can be connected to Cluster 1.OA.C in which children use strategies to add and subtract within 20. In Lesson 8.7, children model tens and ones to add a one-digit number to a two-digit number, which is a direct connection to Cluster 1.OA.A by representing and solving an addition problem. Throughout the remainder of the lessons, children continue adding and subtracting, strengthening the connection between Clusters 1.NBT.C, 1.OA.C, and 1.OA.A.

Building Fluency

Fluency within 1.OA.C.6 continues to be supported within Lessons 8.4–8.10. Children work to use tens and ones to add numbers, solve addition word problems, and add two-digit and one-digit numbers. While children work within Lessons 8.4–8.10, fluency in addition and subtraction within 10 is used as they add ones and tens. Children will use fluency to know when to compose a ten while adding.

The *Personal Math Trainer*'s standards quizzes allow for targeted practice to help build fluency. Use *Personal Math Trainer*: Standards Quiz 1.OA.C.6 to strengthen children's mastery of adding and subtracting within 10.

Chapter 8
Review/Test

Summative Assessment

Use the **Chapter Review/Test** to assess children's progress in Chapter 8.

You may want to review with children the essential question for the chapter.

Chapter Essential Question

How can you add and subtract two-digit numbers?

Ask the following questions to focus children's thinking:

- **What ways can you use tens and ones to add and subtract two-digit numbers?**
- **How can making a ten help you add a two-digit number and a one-digit number?**

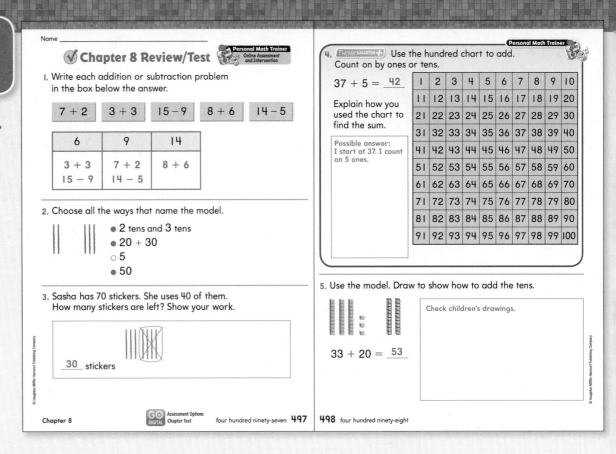

 Data-Driven Decision Making  **RtI** **Chapter 8**

Based on the results of the Chapter Review/Test use the following resources to review skills.

Item	Lesson	Standards	Content Focus	Personal Math Trainer	Intervene With
1, 8	8.1	1.OA.C.6	Use strategies to add and subtract within 20.	1.OA.C.6	R—8.1
2, 9	8.2	1.NBT.C.4	Add tens.	1.NBT.C.4	R—8.2
3	8.3	1.NBT.C.6	Draw models to subtract tens.	1.NBT.C.6	R—8.3
4	8.4	1.NBT.C.4	Use a hundred chart to add.	1.NBT.C.4	R—8.4
5	8.5	1.NBT.C.4	Use models to add ones or tens to a two-digit number.	1.NBT.C.4	R—8.5
6	8.6	1.NBT.C.4	Make a ten to add a two-digit number and a one-digit number.	1.NBT.C.4	R—8.6
7	8.7	1.NBT.C.4	Use place-value models to add two-digit numbers.	1.NBT.C.4	R—8.7
10	8.8	1.NBT.C.4	Solve an addition word problem.	1.NBT.C.4	R—8.8
11	8.9	1.NBT.C.4	Relate addition and subtraction.	1.NBT.C.4	R—8.9
12	8.10	1.NBT.C.4, 1.NBT.C.6	Use different strategies to add and subtract.	1.NBT.C.4, 1.NBT.C.6	R—8.10

Key: R—Reteach (in the *Chapter Resources*)

6. Use the model. Draw to show how to make a ten.

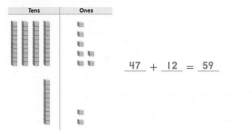

Check children's drawings. Possible drawing shown.

$26 + 7 = \underline{33}$

7. Write the addition sentence that the model shows. Solve.

Tens	Ones

$\underline{47} + \underline{12} = \underline{59}$

8. What is the difference?

$\begin{array}{r} 15 \\ -\ 7 \\ \hline \end{array}$

○ 7 ● 8 ○ 10 ○ 12

9. What is the sum?

$\begin{array}{r} 40 \\ +\ 50 \\ \hline \end{array}$

○ 10 ○ 70 ○ 80 ● 90

10. Luis has 16 .
He has 38 🍂.
How many leaves does Luis have? Circle the number that makes the sentence true.

Luis has ⟨54⟩ leaves.

| 48 |
| 54 |
| 59 |

11. Match the math sentences that count on and back by tens.

$38 + 30 = ?$ $48 + 40 = ?$ $38 + 20 = ?$

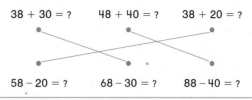

$58 - 20 = ?$ $68 - 30 = ?$ $88 - 40 = ?$

12. **GO DEEPER** Find the sum of 62 and 15. Use any way to add.

$62 + 15 = \underline{77}$

Explain how you solved the problem.

> Check children's answers. Possible answer: I added the 6 tens to 1 ten and added the 2 ones to 5 ones. I did not need to make a ten.

Performance Assessment Task
Chapter 8

See the *Chapter Resources* for a Performance Task that assesses children's understanding of the content of this chapter.

For each task, you will find sample student work for each of the response levels in the task scoring rubric.

Critical Area Performance Assessment Task
Chapters 6-8

See the *Chapter Resources* for a Performance Task that assesses children's understanding of the content of this critical area.

For each task, you will find sample student work for each of the response levels in the task scoring rubric.

Portfolio Performance Assessment Tasks may be used for portfolios.

Be sure to assign children Exercise 4 in the Personal Math Trainer. It features an animation or video to help children model and solve the problem.

Summative Assessment

Use the **Chapter Test** to assess children's progress in Chapter 8.

Chapter Tests are presented in Common Core assessment formats in the *Chapter Resources*.

Personal Math Trainer

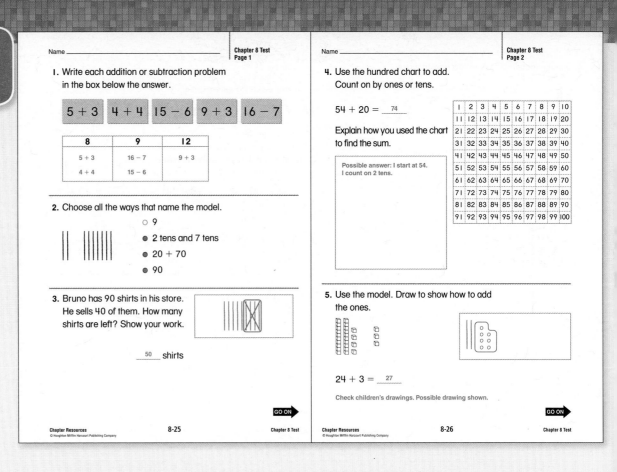

Name _____ Chapter 8 Test Page 1

1. Write each addition or subtraction problem in the box below the answer.

5 + 3   4 + 4   15 − 6   9 + 3   16 − 7

8	9	12
5 + 3	16 − 7	9 + 3
4 + 4	15 − 6	

2. Choose all the ways that name the model.
   ○ 9
   ● 2 tens and 7 tens
   ● 20 + 70
   ● 90

3. Bruno has 90 shirts in his store. He sells 40 of them. How many shirts are left? Show your work.

   _50_ shirts

Chapter Resources
© Houghton Mifflin Harcourt Publishing Company   8-25   Chapter 8 Test   GO ON

Name _____ Chapter 8 Test Page 2

4. Use the hundred chart to add. Count on by ones or tens.

54 + 20 = _74_

Explain how you used the chart to find the sum.

Possible answer: I start at 54. I count on 2 tens.

1	2	3	4	5	6	7	8	9	10
11	12	13	14	15	16	17	18	19	20
21	22	23	24	25	26	27	28	29	30
31	32	33	34	35	36	37	38	39	40
41	42	43	44	45	46	47	48	49	50
51	52	53	54	55	56	57	58	59	60
61	62	63	64	65	66	67	68	69	70
71	72	73	74	75	76	77	78	79	80
81	82	83	84	85	86	87	88	89	90
91	92	93	94	95	96	97	98	99	100

5. Use the model. Draw to show how to add the ones.

24 + 3 = _27_

Check children's drawings. Possible drawing shown.

Chapter Resources
© Houghton Mifflin Harcourt Publishing Company   8-26   Chapter 8 Test   GO ON

✓ Data-Driven Decision Making ▲ RtI

Based on the results of the Chapter Test use the following resources to review skills.

Item	Lesson	Standards	Content Focus	Personal Math Trainer	Intervene With
1, 8	8.1	1.OA.C.6	Use strategies to add and subtract within 20.	1.OA.C.6	R—8.1
2, 9	8.2	1.NBT.C.4	Add tens.	1.NBT.C.4	R—8.2
3	8.3	1.NBT.C.6	Draw models to subtract tens.	1.NBT.C.6	R—8.3
4	8.4	1.NBT.C.4	Use a hundred chart to add.	1.NBT.C.4	R—8.4
5	8.6	1.NBT.C.4	Use models to add ones or tens to a two-digit number.	1.NBT.C.4	R—8.5
6	8.6	1.NBT.C.4	Make a ten to add a two-digit number and a one-digit number.	1.NBT.C.4	R—8.6
7	8.7	1.NBT.C.4	Use place-value models to add two-digit numbers.	1.NBT.C.4	R—8.7
10	8.8	1.NBT.C.4	Solve an addition word problem.	1.NBT.C.4	R—8.8
11	8.9	1.NBT.C.4	Relate addition and subtraction.	1.NBT.C.4	R—8.9
12	8.10	1.NBT.C.4, 1.NBT.C.6	Use different strategies to add and subtract.	1.NBT.C.4, 1.NBT.C.6	R—8.10

Key: R—Reteach (in the *Chapter Resources*)

6. Use the model. Draw to show how to make a ten.

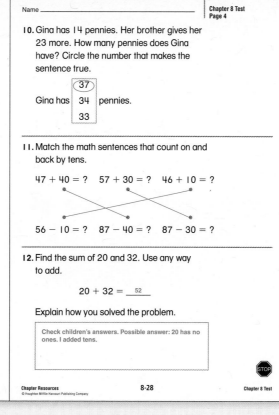

Check children's drawings. Possible drawing shown.

$37 + 6 =$ ___43___

7. Write the addition sentence that the model shows. Solve.

Tens	Ones

___32___ + ___41___ = ___73___

8. What is the difference?

$$\begin{array}{r} 13 \\ -\ 8 \\ \hline \end{array}$$

- ● 5
- ○ 6
- ○ 9
- ○ 10

9. What is the sum?

$$\begin{array}{r} 30 \\ +40 \\ \hline \end{array}$$

- ○ 20
- ○ 50
- ● 70
- ○ 80

GO ON ▶

10. Gina has 14 pennies. Her brother gives her 23 more. How many pennies does Gina have? Circle the number that makes the sentence true.

Gina has [37 / **34** / 33] pennies.

11. Match the math sentences that count on and back by tens.

$47 + 40 = ?$ $57 + 30 = ?$ $46 + 10 = ?$

$56 - 10 = ?$ $87 - 40 = ?$ $87 - 30 = ?$

12. Find the sum of 20 and 32. Use any way to add.

$20 + 32 =$ ___52___

Explain how you solved the problem.

Check children's answers. Possible answer: 20 has no ones. I added tens.

STOP

Portfolio Suggestions

The portfolio represents the growth, talents, achievements, and reflections of the mathematics learner. Children might spend a short time selecting work samples for their portfolios.

You may want to have children respond to the following questions:

- What new understanding of math have I developed in the past several weeks?
- What growth in understanding or skills can I see in my work?
- What can I do to improve my understanding of math ideas?
- What would I like to learn more about?

For information about how to organize, share, and evaluate portfolios, see the *Chapter Resources*

Chapter 8 Test

Chapter 8 Test   500B